PORTRAIT OF A RIVER

THE RIVER SWERE IN OXFORDSHIRE

by

Walter L. Meagher and Peter Sheasby

Photographs by Peter Sheasby

ENGLISH LANDSCAPES

Bloxham, Oxfordshire

Funding support from the Local Heritage Initiative.

Maps drawn by: Anghelen Phillips (pages 84, 107, 120, 122, 133, 139, 148, 164), Blenheim Colour (page 7), Edith Gollnast (page 167) and Wendy Meagher (pages 8, 17, 53, 72)

Illustrations by Wendy Meagher (pages 49, 109)

Photographs on pages 14, 34 by Walter L. Meagher; page 147 by Sylvie Nickels

Botanical Latin and English common names follow Clive Stace, 1999, *Field Flora of the British Isles*, Cambridge University Press.

Cover photograph: Characteristically narrow and winding, the River Swere in its upper course.

Designed by Wendy Meagher

Scanning, layout and production by Blenheim Colour Ltd, Eynsham, Oxford

Typeset in Garamond and Gill

Printed by Information Press Ltd, Eynsham, Oxford

Local Heritage *initiative*

FOREWORD

The narrow valleys of the River Swere are places of moist and dry woods, marshes fed by springs, calcareous grasslands and old hay meadows rich in wildflowers, trees, shrubs and butterflies. England is a treasury of small rivers. The smallest are the least attended; we know our highways better than our rivers. In this book, one small river is given a public voice, a place at the table of community affairs.

Often we may not know nature at hand, what birds live concealed at the river's shores or what plants live in the woods and marshes by its sides. 'I find these tiny streams,' David Bellamy writes, 'the most exciting places to visit in any landscape … oases of semi-naturalness in an otherwise man-managed landscape.'[1]

Conservation is a bond with nature, an attitude towards the past, and a necessity for survival. The valley of the River Swere in the Oxfordshire Uplands has a natural heritage that includes plants and historical artefacts. Nine water-mill sites were inventoried for William the Conqueror in 1087. Each water-mill has altered the river and, like stone barrows and ridge-and-furrow fields, the leats are evidence of a time-bound and historic technology, and a part of the local heritage.

Gilbert White of Selborne thought it not 'unentertaining' to list the rare plants of his part of England in 1778.[2] Were he to list all the plants he knew, he feared to try the reader's patience and inflict a chore more than bestow a pleasure. We have the same challenge, and feel a certain urgency, as if at any moment an old meadow, with a marsh by its spring and twenty-two species of wildflowers within its province, might be excavated for new urban services.

Portrait of a River reveals a wealth of plant life neither of us knew we would discover so close to home and so near the Banbury to Chipping Norton road. At the same time, compiling plant lists, complete with common and Latin names, is an earnest endeavour. They urge the Sherlock Holmes and Doctor Watsons of nature to track habitats for gains and losses in their wildflower species composition. Nature is not static; not only do mountains move but fences fall and uses of the land change.

Wherever we could, we followed public footpaths; the meandering river is easily seen from paths that cross the meadows beside it, but not every attraction of nature is visible from a right-of-way. The cooperation of landowners has been essential – we sought explicit permission to view the river on private land, and no landowner turned us away.

Portrait of a River is an incentive to adventure but not specifically a guide for walking, nor do we endorse in any way walking on a person's land without consent. A useful reference for walks in this part of the Oxfordshire Uplands is the OS (Ordnance Survey) 191 Explorer Map. Of the 29 wetland, 14 meadow and 8 woodland sites visited, none has a proper name, but we have, like explorers on a new shore, christened each one.

The British Isles please the country walker with a variety of prospects, with a local topography so eventful it seems more the effect of manorial management than of a tormented earth. Coming to the same places in all seasons, to the wood below the SSSI (Site of Special Scientific Interest), to The Meanders and the Barford valley, one appreciates that the Swere is the spine of an anthology of landscapes and a collection of stories everyone may share.

Young people should be encouraged to come out of their urban places, sequestered from yellowhammers and bulrush marshes, to go on country walks. From a greater familiarity with local scenes may arise an affectionate disposition towards nature. This disposition, so favourable to effective conservation, we share with our readers in words and photographs.

TABLE OF CONTENTS

INTRODUCING THE RIVER SWERE

LIKE BIRDS AND CLOUDS, rivers move incessantly, but they move in a channel, which changes slowly, sometimes imperceptibly. A river is 'a copious stream of water flowing in a channel towards the sea, a lake, or another stream',[3] or it 'may be defined to be the surplus of rainfall over evaporation'[4]; it carries silt and sediment, crab apples and ash leaves, and the dreams of men. Rivers are more ancient than nations and facilitate the foundation and extension of cultures, but also their 'mere existence … makes the world a more attractive and a more interesting place'.[5]

Rivers work constantly to abrade the land. As if it must balance an equation, what the river takes away from one bank it puts down against another, all the while moving suspended silts seawards; rivers reduce the land more effectively than any other agent. The ground level of the world, it is estimated, is worn down by 8 mm per century, a rate that is sufficient to remove all the existing continental relief in 25,000,000 years.[6] All other forces of the erosion of the interior landscapes – ice, wind and rain – work intermittently, except the ocean, which, lashing the shore, has the same constancy.

The River Swere is narrow, shallow and shy. It is easily overlooked, yet being neighbours, we decided to improve our acquaintance, and learn how it conducted its business. There were surprises: How could there be such a variety of habitat and plant life in valleys so tiny? There are 29 marshy wetland places with 109 kinds of vascular plants, never before discovered in their entirety. They are a book of nature and compose an anthology of stories, each species making a contribution to the community of life we call its habitat.

To each village belongs a part of the river, where walks are taken. Villagers are the river's naturalists. Let them keep a notebook and observe the rise and fall in fish populations, the frequency of rare birds such as snipe, and of any change in the abundance of plant life. They will be the Gilbert Whites of the Swere, and never think that their jottings will be of no value. To examine a river this way, is to know better where one lives. When Speke asked, 'Whence the Nile?', he found Lake Victoria. We asked, 'Whence the Swere?', and found a spring next to a badger sett. Only the scale is different.

Right: A map of Oxfordshire county, showing the principal towns and villages along the River Swere and the River Cherwell.

Banbury

Bloxham Adderbury

Hook Norton *River Swere*

Deddington

Chipping Norton

River Cherwell

Woodstock

OXFORDSHIRE

Oxford

River Thames

Abingdon

Wallingford

River Thames

Oxford • London

Northern tributaries
Hook
Norton   Wigginton

Milcombe

South
Newington   Barford St John   *River Swere*

River Swere   Barford St Michael   Deddington

Swerford   *River Cherwell*

Priory Mill
Kiteney Copse

N

2 miles

About the River Swere

The Swere arises in obscurity from two springs, one higher than the other, on a steep hill in a secondary wood called Kiteney Copse. Not every outpouring of earth's water can be the site of a Roman villa, but Chedworth, in Gloucestershire, has a spring no more forceful nor more voluminous in its issue than Kiteney Copse. At the mouth of both springs are deposits of tufa, a porous calcium carbonate rock formed when the $CaCO_3$ is precipitated by turbulence, and sometimes by a biological agent; but only by the larger spring is there the telltale heaped earth of a badger sett.

The Swere first flows north, being at the will of the slope of the land, reaching the first reservoir at Priory Mill. Afterwards it turns east-north-east, making its way to the River Cherwell, a journey from which it is never deflected.

In most places in the upper course of the river one may easily vault the stream, but where it is wider a crossing is not so easy. In The Dingle (page 132) a fallen oak tree bridges the river and challenges the daredevil; with less courage, one may cross a wide reach of the river over a footbridge in Barford St Michael. The width of the Swere varies from 1 to 4 m, and it is wider downstream just as it is narrower above Wigginton, for that is the very nature of a river and not a property peculiar to the Swere.

It is not true that depth varies consistently on a gradient from shallow upstream to deep downstream, but where the river is shallow upstream the least depth is 4 cm; where it is deepest in the dry season, when our measurements were made, it is 1 – 1.2 m deep. 'Swere', in Anglo-Saxon, means slow, sluggish; the name fits its character, which we suppose has not changed in historic times. After a long dry period, the river downstream is choked with branched bur-reed (*Sparganium erectum*), and moves languorously, or may not seem to move at all.

Alternately lax and robust, the Swere has been carving the valley from Swerford to the River Cherwell, since the retreat of the Oxford glaciers 10,000 years ago. In the post-glacial period, 'heavy local snowfall must have led to floods in spring probably many times greater than those fed by present rains'.[7] But even now, the autumn-winter river, with sudden heavy inputs of water, disputes the Anglo-Saxon name and, as expected, while cutting banks more vigorously, it transports heavier sediment loads in December than in August.

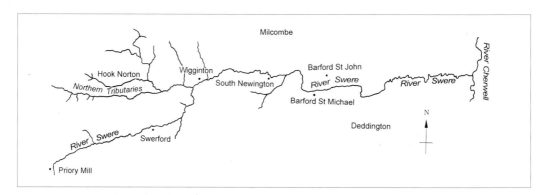

Map of the River Swere, showing the dendritic pattern of the river's drainage network. Side streams are plentiful in the upper course where the hills are steep and close to the river.

The Swere is 25.3 km (15.8 miles) long. If it were a straight line, it would be half this length. Where it is most straight it is least interesting because meandering creates a beauty of curving forms. The river is deeper on the bends of meanders than in straight sections between the bends. Pools and shallows alternate, in response to the substrate – limestone or clay – and depth varies across the channel as well as along it.

Occasionally, autumn rainfall is so heavy the river quickly rises and floods its banks. Here, on the Barford Bridge, the water has risen not from the river beneath the bridge, but from its old course just about where the road curves, towards the top of the photograph. A map showing the old course of the river is in the Oak Field Marshes chapter (see page 139).

The Gradient of the Land

The Swere arises at about 198 m asl (above sea level) (data taken from the OS 191 map), and falls 31 m in the short distance (1.1 km) it travels to Bulrush Pond below Priory Mill. At Priory Mill Pond, which is about 168 m asl, the river turns east; by the time it passes under the Banbury Road at South Newington it has fallen 46 m in 11.6 km. Reaching the ford at South Newington, the river has travelled just slightly less than half its length. From here, in the last phase of its journey from South Newington to the Cherwell River, the slope of the land continues to lessen, and the River Swere becomes a wide valley river and falls only a further 30 m.

The River and Parish Boundaries

In the history of mankind, rivers have separated tribe from tribe, and nation from nation. For example, the Dobunni, a tribe east of the River Cherwell, before the Roman Conquest, viewed the Cherwell as their western boundary. We have no evidence that the Swere performed such a function, but it has long been called upon to bound parishes: Great Rollright from Over Norton, Swerford from Great Rollright, Hook Norton and Wigginton; Wigginton from South Newington; South Newington from Milcombe; Bloxham from Barford St Michael; Barford St John from Deddington; and Deddington from Adderbury.

Geology of the Swere

In the upper course, the Swere lies in a concavity of land between the Rollright Fault and the Swerford Fault.[8] This concavity overlies Great Oolite Limestone; the deeper beds are mainly clay, clay-silts and siltstones. When a chalk land bridge joined England to France, the River Thames was a tributary of the Rhine! An unimaginable thickness of sediments has been deposited during untold ages in a primeval sea, and now clays and silts lie about 30.5 m thick below the coursing Swere. At a greater depth still, there is more clay, three times that thickness, accumulations which represent only one age in earth's history, the Jurassic. Day by day, without change of shift, the river digs the clay away.

Passing the alluvium of the floodplain wood west of Swerford Park, the river changes and becomes shallow. For the first time in its length, the channel is sand and gravel (bedded on Chipping Norton Limestone) encouraging the river to riffle and chatter. It is never so shallow again. Downstream from the Park, including all the land of the Swerford and Wigginton marshes, the foundation of the topsoils is clay, silts and sandstones. As a result, in these places there are pools and the river is often deeper.

Chipping Norton Limestone underlies the site of the Roman Villa above Wigginton and is the source of the soil chemistry favouring limestone grasslands on the northern and southern slopes of the river from west of Wigginton, above The Meanders and east towards South Newington. Limestone soil favours a variety of plants including common knapweed (*Centaurea nigra*), meadow saxifrage (*Saxifraga granulata*) and salad burnet (*Sanguisorba minor* spp. *minor*), in some cases attracting butterflies and insects special to them. The occurrence of these plants is a clear signal, one that the country walker learns to read, that the substrate is the product of the compression of the shells of the ancient ocean's molluscan inhabitants; but farther on the substrate changes. Above Long Marsh and Pond, which is an old hay meadow with some wildflower species common to the Wigginton meadow (common knapweed but not meadow saxifrage), the substrate is Marlstone Rock.

Again the river follows a fault, always seeking the way of least resistance. From The Dingle to the Cherwell, the Swere runs between two fault lines, bounded by the Barford St John Fault on the north side and the Barford St Michael Fault on the south. But the character of the channel is more affected by the soils underlying it than by the concavity between the fault lines, a geology that is a layer of formations: Marlstone Rock bed, clay, silts and siltstones; then from the Barfords to the Cherwell, the substrate is principally clay, silts and siltstones.

Entering Swerford Park, the river is shallow, providing a crossing for the hunt. In no other section of its 25.3 km length is the riverbed so gravelly. Tufa encrustations appear on the rocks, whitened by calcium carbonate, as seen in the lower left-hand corner of this photograph. Out of the frame of the picture, the hill on its right-hand side rises steeply, and is richly wooded with mature beech trees.

River Profiles

One of the special aspects of 'doing the River Swere' has been the part played by volunteers from South Newington parish. On 13 April 2003, Tara Bailey, Keith Loban and Philippa Richards chose three places near South Newington to measure the width of the river, its rate of flow and to diagram river profiles. Flow was measured at 10 m intervals, and an average rate of flow was computed for each site.

Measurements of the River Swere			
SP	Width (cm)	Depth (cm)	Flow (metre/second)
355 426	430	15	0.62
384 422	470	26	0.48
355 411	410	50	0.20

The river pulses: the measurements show that the river is fastest where it is most shallow. The rate of flow depends on the depth of the channel, the friction of the streambed – varying with gravel or clay – and the gradient of the land. Thomas Hardy renders the mood of a small stream in its slack season:

> Reticulations creep upon the slack stream's face,
> When the wind skims irritably past.

> from *On Sturminster Foot-bridge*

In the first profile, the channel is deep only on one side; in the third one, the form of the channel more nearly approaches the shape of a ship's hull. It is wrong to think that 'science knows' or that what is theoretically easy to do therefore need not be done. The entire river could be diagrammed; one has only to decide the intervals, and put on one's hip boots.

River Depth and Water-Lilies

The Swere is fed by springs and seeps and by run-off from the fields and hills adjoining it. In June, the river depth has fallen by a multiple of three since March; by November it is a bulge of foam breaking over its banks. The rapidly moving stream presses down the channel-clogging vegetation of summer, carrying seaward leaf, branch and fallen apple; village fields are silted and roads flooded. Large flowering plants with floating leaves, such as the white and yellow water-lilies, are adapted to changes in water depth, but not to turbidity.

Profiles of the River Swere in its middle course, made in South Newington parish.

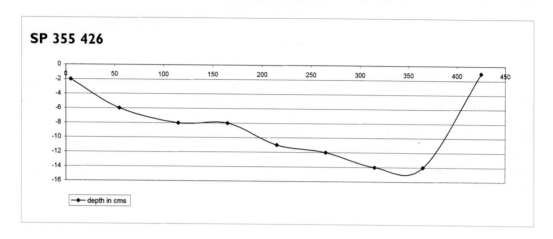

SP 355 426

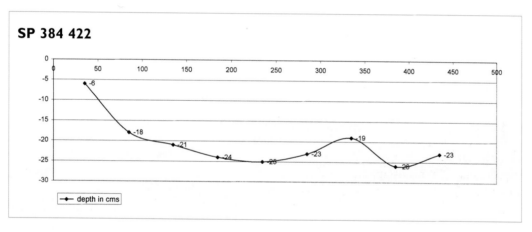

SP 384 422

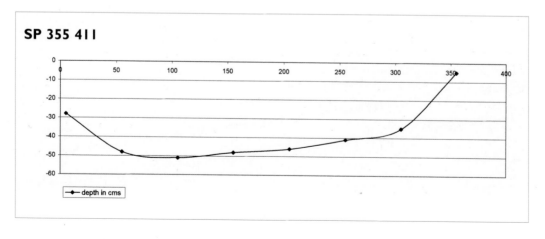

SP 355 411

Jan	Feb	Mar	Apr	May	Jun	Jul	Aug	Sep	Oct	Nov	Dec
19	35	24	15	11	7	4	4	2	10	33	30

The above measurements were made in South Newington in 2002 by Bob McCall, who has for a long time kept rainfall and water depth data, and who also provided the information for the charts on the previous page. In another year the figures would be different, but the pattern much the same. The white water-lily (*Nymphaea alba*) and yellow water-lily (*Nuphar lutea*) flower and fruit when the water is low and the current slow. They have long stems – the white varies from 0.5 to 3 m in length; the yellow ranges up to 2 m. The Swere is never too deep for them, but if it were a rushing torrent in all seasons, these plants of such exceptional floral beauty would no longer be available to please us.

Each species of aquatic plant has its own level of tolerance for violent wave action. Below Adderbury Bridge, in the four summer months, there are rafts of common duckweed (*Lemna minor*) and, less commonly, agglomerations of water-starwort (*Callitriche* sp.), becalmed in water almost without motion. Where silts form a footing on the river's edge, branched bur-reed is common. Then, when the river rages in November and December, their long stems (to 1.5 m) and keeled leaves are pressed under water; summer's river species disappear and the choked channel is unblocked.

The bridge of Barford St Michael.

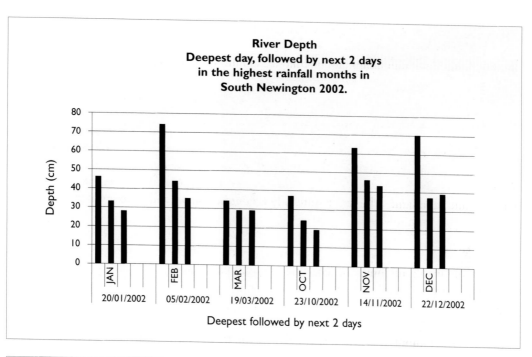

The efficiency of the river channel is demonstrated by the data exhibited in these bar graphs. With heavy rainfall and rapid run-off from the fields and tributary streams the river rises rapidly, as shown on the first day in each of the three-day sequences. But if the rainstorm abates, the water-level falls just as rapidly, demonstrating the efficiency of the channel, dug out and kept clear of obstruction by the Environment Agency.

Left: June's river has stalled. It is as still as a pond where, east of Little Barford Mill and close to Deddington parish, colonies of yellow water-lily (*Nuphar lutea*) flower each year. The tall grass on the bank, coming into flower, is reed sweet-grass (*Glyceria maxima*), and the straight stems, some bent, behind the yellow water-lily, is branched bur-reed (*Sparganium erectum*).

Below: The large showy flower of the white water-lily (*Nymphaea alba*) rises in the midst of its large floating leaves. The leaves are attached to the rhizome by a long petiole; the flower is borne singly on a long stalk and has many petals. Rarely, some leaves rise out of the water. Yellow water-lily has both floating and submerged leaves.

Highlights of the Journey Downstream

Settlement in the Swere valley, and on the nearby hills, has been continuous for over 2,000 years. From archaeologists, we know that the 'rich red soil and the River Swere ... attracted Romano-British settlers'[9] before the Anglo-Saxons and Normans.

The River Swere from start to finish passes under nine roads, skirts the settlements of six ancient villages and is divided into upper, middle and lower courses. In the upper course (sections A–E), the river is narrow and shallow (there are exceptions); steep hills on both sides are not far from the channel; the valleys are narrow; and grey willow (*Salix cinerea*) and hazel (*Corylus avellana*) are common. In the middle course (F–I), the land on either side of the river is much less wooded; intermittently the valley widens, usually on only one side; and limestone grassland and lowland marshes support a generous variety of herbaceous species. The lower course (J–K) is not wider than the river in the middle course but it has been dug out more often by the former River Authority; the adjoining fields are used for arable crops, grain and oilseed rape more than for pasture and turnip.

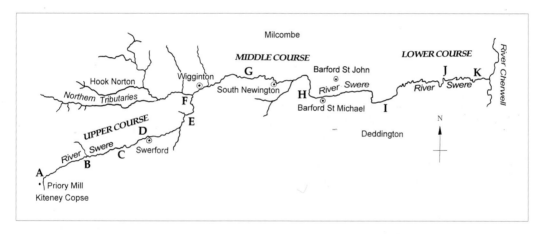

The upper, middle and lower courses of the River Swere. These spaces are not sharply bounded on the map, and are in any case approximate; the SP numbers in the text locate the boundaries of each segment.

Upper Course

A. The river's source to Bulrush Marsh (SP 334 294 to 333 303)

Flowing north and downhill from its source at two springs in Kiteney Copse, the calcium-rich water of the Swere passes through ponds and marshes, and is momentarily delayed at the Priory Mill Pond before coursing on to Bulrush Marsh.

B. Juncus Marshes to Hook Norton Road (SP 333 303 to 344 306)

Turning east, the river passes Juncus Marshes and Heron Pond. Along its way, grey willow and hazel are dominant. Passing a pond checkered with broad-leaved pondweed, the river journeys to the junction of Heythrop Road and the Hook Norton Road.

C. From Hook Norton Road to Ashwood and Clearwater Pond (SP 344 306 to 355 312)

Ashwood, the hawthorn thicket from across the river, and Clearwater Pond are marked on the OS 191 map. Fallen and broken limbs criss-cross the narrow river, compressed by the proximity of the adjoining hills, as it passes through Hazel Terrace Wood, past Clearwater Pond, which lies opposite the Swere Bank SSSI, and on to the Hook Norton Road.

D. From the Floodplain Wood to Between Towns (SP 355 312 to 374 313)

Passing through Floodplain Wood the river soon enters Swerford Park, where for a moment it becomes wide, shallow and chattering. In the Park it is dammed to form a long lake, and it then passes on through Church Marsh.

E. Between Towns to Paradise Farm (SP 374 313 to 387 323)

East of a small floodplain, for the first time there is a wider valley and a variety of marshes. Opposite Island Marsh and Pond there is a beech wood on a steep slope; in the river are tufa dams. Past Mint Marsh are old white willow trees.

Middle Course
F. Quarry Spring Marsh to Wigginton (SP 387 323 to 396 330)

Changes begun at Swerford are amplified: the valley is wider, there is more wet meadow and the river edge is unwooded. At the head of the valley, the Hook Norton stream (also called the northern tributary) joins the Swere and flows towards the Wigginton mill. Ribbon Marsh is formed in the channel of the ancient river.

G. The Meanders to Banbury Road, South Newington (SP 396 330 to 407 334)

Wildflowers in dense stands, including meadow saxifrage and salad burnet, grow in the moist grassland north of the river in the valley of The Meanders. In the Milcombe valley, springs sustain a greater number of ponds and marshes, with herbaceous species special to them, more than will ever be seen again along the Swere.

H. South Newington to the Bloxham Road, Barford St Michael (SP 407 334 to 437 329)

Now the river is straight, and alder dominant, from the ford to The Dingle. Then it meanders again, is wider, and has a few big trees, including a sweet, or Spanish, chestnut, at the base of a steep hill in The Dingle. From there, the river is a long canal, carrying water to the mill at Barford St Michael.

I. Barford St Michael to Deddington and past Hazel Wood (SP 437 329 to 462 333)

From the bridge, the river reverts to meandering; soon it is checked and reformed as a canal advancing to Little Barford Mill, a picturesque ruin. Below the mill pond, the river meanders again, and alder reclaims a place on the river bank. Art follows nature in this characteristically pastoral landscape of the Midlands, with low hill-sheltered pastures and grazing sheep fat on early summer grass.

Lower Course

J. Hazel Wood to Paper Mill Cottages (SP 462 333 to 478 335)

More a deep watery ditch than a coursing stream, the river edge is unwooded but dotted at wide intervals with crack-willow and alder trees. Below Adderbury Bridge is the river's only stand of perfoliate pondweed. East of the bridge, the river finally takes a straight course toward Paper Mill on Adderbury Grounds Farm.

K. To the confluence with the River Cherwell (SP 478 335 to 493 338)

East of Paper Mill, sycamore trees shade the river and gypsywort grows on its shores. For a short distance, low hills compress the river's shore and then farther downstream the valley becomes wider. Trees are less frequent, the river more a shallow stream in a deep ditch.

In summer sunlight, the River Swere meanders slowly, wider here than above or below this reach east of Little Barford Mill, perfectly representative of the river's middle course.

VILLAGE CHURCHES

THE PARISH CHURCHES of England signify the triumph of Christianity so widespread and so enduring in its visual effect that it is difficult to imagine Swerford before St Mary stood above its decayed motte and bailey, Wigginton before St Giles gave a distinctive shape to the village skyline, especially from east of the village, or South Newington before St Peter ad Vincula was built to preside over the village with easy authority. But we might try to remember there was a time, little documented in the historical record, when Christianity had no monuments in the River Swere valleys.

'The popular idea of an English village is of one in a valley, where it can be overlooked from the hills, clustered about its ancient church.'[10] This expectation is generally realized in the Swere valleys. Except Swerford, which is on a hill, and the valley which is below the church; otherwise, Wigginton, South Newington and the Barfords may be overlooked from adjoining hills. Men made a mark on English landscapes long before Christianity. For example, 'Few parish churches of the seventh or eighth century have left remains which can now be identified.'[11]

St Peter ad Vincula, South Newington, in winter.

Two views of St Mary, Swerford:

Left: A close view of the village church, with a billowing border of red valerian (*Centranthus ruber*). The west tower of St Mary, evidently *ca* 1300, is capped by a six-sided spire.

Below: St Mary's in its village setting; the church spire rises above the fellowship of cottages and houses in a landscape of wooded hills and upland pastures.

St Giles, Wigginton. 'Wigginton is a rectory, the patronage of which is now in the hands of the Principal, Fellows and Scholars of Jesus College, Oxford. It is now held in conjunction with the benefices of Hook Norton, Swerford, and Great Rollright.'[12]

Not far from the Swere is a chambered long barrow, near Steeple Barton, and another, southeast of Chipping Norton in Enstone Plantation. Evidence of settlement in North Oxfordshire before Christianity is common, and, one supposes, there were forms of worship, superstition and godhead. The Gauls, Jutes, Danes, Angles and Frisians brought their gods to England and insisted on having 'temples, and priests, and sacrifices of their own'.[13] In Oxfordshire there were very few parish churches before the eleventh century, and the first local churches were attached to manor houses.

Simultaneously in town and country there came a boom in church-building. It began under King Cnut and Edward the Confessor, and received its greatest stimulus from the Norman Conquest. But parish churches in the Swere valleys came later. The first, built almost 100 years after the Conquest, was the parish church at Barford St Michael (1160), showing a fusion of Anglo-Saxon and Norman decorative forms – acanthus foliage on the capitals and biting heads around the doorway arch.[14] The boom continued to the mid-twelfth century: churches at Barford St John, South Newington, Hook Norton and Deddington are all of the twelfth century; the last to be founded, by 1300, were the churches at Swerford and Wigginton. It is from that time that the most prominent feature of village skylines was formed and remains constant to today.

Walking along footpaths near the river, within sight of any of these churches, one enjoys seeing a familiar tower just as much as seeing meadow flowers or a distant wood. They are all of a piece, as in a painting, and yet each church is distinctive – in the form of the chancel, the height of the tower, spire or pinnacles, the size, timbre and number of the bells, whether there are wall-paintings, and the size and age of the font; but they follow a common plan, and share in the greater unity of all the parish churches of England. The details of architecture and furnishings are well and good, but to the rambler, and the Sunday walker, the village church is as alluring to the pencil as it is to the eye, and contributes to a landscape in which it is a central feature.

The parish church at Barford St Michael is sited on high ground, behind the photographer, giving a view of Barford Manor on the alluvial plain near the river.

PRIORY MILL AND KITENEY COPSE

NO OTHER MILL is so isolated, or so elevated, with a buzzard's eye-view of the narrow valley below and of the hills of Great Rollright parish to the north, as Priory Mill. Recorded in Domesday Book (1087), the mill belonged to 'Cold Norton Priory', of the Augustinian Order, in the thirteenth century. By 1871 there was a thirty-acre farm called Priory Mill, with a miller and two men. The Chipping Norton Steam Granary operated the mill in the 1930s but it fell into disuse as the worldwide depression lowered demand for grain. Priory Mill was reborn as a private residence with a beautiful garden and a year-round window on wild nature.

The mill pond at Priory Mill is a splendid ornament to the house and a habitat attracting roe deer and kingfishers.

The River Swere arises in Kiteney Copse from two small springs. At first a trickle of water, perhaps a gush in some seasons, spreads wide like a fan, and is for a short distance unconfined by a fixed channel. The air is moist and the ground is mossy; lichens cover branches, bark and stones. There are few flowering plants.

Enlarged by the congregation of surface water across the steep slope, and by the flow from the second spring nearly at the same height as the badger sett that is there, the Swere swells, grows ambitious and fixes a channel.

Kiteney Copse may once have been a mature woodland; now it is a secondary wood with a dense and tangling understorey of shrubs. Blackthorn (*Prunus spinosa*) grows in light gaps; grey willow (*Salix cinerea*) and hazel (*Corylus avellana*) are common – these two species frequent the riverside all the way to the Wigginton valley. Other woody species occur occasionally: apple (*Malus* agg.), ash (*Fraxinus excelsior*), buckthorn (*Rhamnus cathartica*), field maple (*Acer campestre*) and sycamore (*A. pseudoplatanus*) join the wood, but tall trees are never abundant. Deep in the wood, where green and great spotted woodpeckers are breeding, marsh-marigold (*Caltha palustris*) thrives in rich black mud, and four species of fern are found: polypody (*Polypodium vulgare*), male-fern (*Dryopteris filix-mas*), broad buckler-fern (*D. dilatata*) and lady-fern (*Athyrium filix-femina*).

Tufa

The Swere is a calcium-rich river in its upper course. Tufa forming deposits at the mouth of the two springs is an indicator of this richness. Tufa was mined at Priory Mill during World War II, and aroused a different interest in the 1970s, when a team of geographers investigated the tufa deposits on land that 'consists of Upper Jurassic Limestone overlying effectually impermeable Upper Lias Clay'.[15]

We invited Dr Heather Viles and Professor Andrew Goudie of the School of Geography, University of Oxford, to bring a group of master's degree students to the Swere to take water samples and make profiles of the river. They came on a dry day in February 2003. At one site, just below the bridge east of the SSSI on the Hook Norton Road, the river banks were firm, the river depth was 18 cm, the pH was about 7.8, and there were tufa deposits on stone and wood. *Vaucheria*, an algal indicator of $CaCO_3$-rich waters, was attached to a large rock above the bridge. Later, working downstream by the beech wood in the Island Marsh and Pond field, a tufa dam (the first of three) was found, the size and shape of a large, finely finished stone structure. At first, it was thought to be a concrete slab, so perfectly had it been formed by the slow action of chemical precipitation.

Ponds and Marshes of Kiteney Copse

In Appendix I, the plants of Swere marshes and ponds above Priory Mill site are grouped as follows: (1) Tufa Ponds in Kiteney Copse; (2) Mare's-tail Pond; and (3) Horsetail and Priory Mill Ponds. The Tufa Ponds, now more dry than wet, were places where excavations were made on the slope of Kiteney Copse, a short distance below the source of the river, probably to mine tufa; in time they have filled with marshy vegetation. In one site, the marsh shows a common pattern of plant zonation. There are three zones: the inner zone is dominated by sedge (*Carex* sp.), the next by hemp-agrimony (*Eupatorium cannabinum*), and the outer edge is shared equally by reed canary-grass (*Phalaris arundinacea*) and tufted hair-grass (*Deschampsia cespitosa*). When the workings were left, water filled the spaces, and became, within the memory of the landowner, her childhood swimming hole. Ponds and marshes in Kiteney Copse are close to each other and seem to form a chain of wetlands, knotted together by the threading river.

Mare's-tail Pond and Marsh

The marsh is a shallow (3–6 cm) pond, distinguished by a species that occurs nowhere else along the Swere: mare's-tail (*Hippuris vulgaris*). This is an ancient British plant, known to have grown in Oxfordshire before the last Ice Age. *Hippuris*, with unbranched stems, whorled leaves and inconspicuous flowers, is a calciophile (calcium lover) which accounts for its occurrence here, a short distance below the springs, where the river is richest in calcium. There are so many mare's-tails in the shallow water, that from a distance the pond looks populated by tall slender pencils. Not far from Kiteney Copse and Priory Mill, mare's-tail grows in proximity to springs on limestone land at the Ditchley and Wychwood estates, and at Glyme Farm, near the Swere catchment. Broad-leaved pondweed (*Potamogeton natans*) is also common in the shallow waters of Mare's-tail Pond and Marsh; common club-rush (*Schoenoplectus lacustris*) stands in stately clumps on the marsh edge.

Horsetail Marsh and Pond

This wetland site is shaped like a bent light bulb, with a wide top and a narrow bottom, and with distinct and strongly demarcated zones of vegetation. Walking into the marsh from the eastern side, reed canary-grass, with tufted vetch (*Vicia cracca*), dominates the outer zone. Next there is a zone of a 'large tufted glabrous perennial 100–160 cm'[16] – greater pond-sedge (*Carex riparia*) – dense, extensive and locally dominant. *Carex riparia* gives way to the locally dominant marsh horsetail (*Equisetum palustre*), which, in turn, is succeeded by a zone of botanical amity in which marsh horsetail and greater pond-sedge share the open space. There is still another zone: tall slender blades of lesser bulrush (*Typha angustifolia*). The bulrush forms a curtain between the plants behind us and the open water that lies ahead. Coming out on to this edge, after crossing the marsh, one sees that the pond connects by a narrow stream – the river! – to the mill pond.

On the outer edge of the open water is hemp-agrimony, attractive to many butterflies, and tufted hair-grass, one of Oxfordshire's most ornamental wild grasses; below the water's surface is common water-starwort (*Callitriche stagnalis*). Shading the water is grey willow, the commonest tree of the river edges in the upper Swere.

Priory Mill Pond

At the base of the chain of copse-side marshes, collecting, holding and widely spreading the waters of the river, is the mill pond. An ornament of the private residence, large, circular, neatly bounded by a mown lawn, and supremely picturesque, it is a garden pond worthy of Chelsea. Vanished is the water-wheel where herons fish and moorhens visit. Common bistort (*Persicaria bistorta*) and amphibious bistort (*Persicaria amphibia*) have rooted by the pond; invasive alien plants, Canadian waterweed (*Elodea canadensis*) and curly waterweed (*Lagarosiphon major*), congest and darken the still, deep aqueous medium. Canadian waterweed, favouring still or sluggish water, was first reported from Great Britain in 1842 and spread rapidly after 1850. A curtain of water falls over the worn oak sluice gate where lady's-mantle (*Alchemilla mollis*) – a garden escape – has rooted in an accumulation of soil in the worn woodwork. At the southern end is reed sweet-grass (*Glyceria maxima*); along the western side there are cow parsley (*Anthriscus sylvestris*), greater tussock-sedge (*Carex paniculata*), hairy sedge (*C. hirta*), lesser pond-sedge (*C. acutiformis*) and yellow iris (*Iris pseudacorus*).

The mill pond releases the stream at the old sluice gate, the liberated water pouring downhill into Bulrush Marsh. The river now sets a new course – east-north-east – and acquires the form it will retain, running in a channel sometimes sinuous, often straight (being 'corrected' by mill-owners of bygone days), until it meets the River Cherwell and becomes the unifying force in landscapes of ancient villages, modest farm fields, hazel woods and hay meadows.

Supremely ornamental, a single greater tussock-sedge (*Carex paniculata*) stands in the shallow water of the far eastern side of the mill pond.

Top left: The Swere, without a strongly formed channel, near the springs from which it arises.

Top right: The river has found its channel, which it will not relinquish until joining the Cherwell 25.3 km (15.8 miles) downstream.

Bottom left: Characteristic secondary growth in Kiteney Copse with marsh-marigold (*Caltha palustris*) in the foreground.

Bottom right: Two aquatic herbs, broad-leaved pondweed (*Potamogeton natans*) and curly waterweed (*Lagarosiphon major*), lying flat on the water and covering it almost completely, with mare's-tail (*Hippuris vulgaris*) sending up its narrow linear stems from stout creeping rhizomes.

CLEARWATER AND HERON PONDS

TRAVELLERS REFER to the Atlantic Ocean as 'the pond'; in North America, every inland lake is a pond. By Oxfordshire standards, Walden Pond in Massachusetts – where Thoreau wrote his meditation on making a home in the woods – is a large lake, and now a public swimming facility. In the UK, a pond is 'a fairly small body of still water … formed artificially by hollowing or embanking'.[17] Ponds and rivers have no natural alliance; most ponds are located away from rivers in morainal dips or flat and low-lying places. But the Swere, for a third of its course, is on a slope and its valley sides are generally narrow to compressed, yet it is a 'pondy' river. Most of its ponds are man-made, and all, small and large, like Clearwater Pond, shown in three views on the opposite page, are sustained by springs.

The best view available to the public is from the high hill north of the river – from the summit of a rich calcareous grassland protected as an SSSI. Seen from this hill, Clearwater Pond is like a jade eye set in a green wood; it stands above the level of the river, held up like a bowl, and is almost perfectly oval in form. Ash (*Fraxinus excelsior*) trees of Swere Bank Wood, on the far horizon, are nearly uniform in height. In the middle photograph, the pond surface, so far uninhabited by water-lily or pondweed, is smooth like the fascia of a gemstone. In the photograph's foreground, common bulrush (*Typha latifolia*) and common club-rush (*Schoenoplectus lacustris*) flourish in the fresh water emptying into the pond from a spring and a stream. A plastic pipe carries water from the pond to the meandering river in the dark wood below.

Both Clearwater and Heron ponds are secluded, remote from the houses that initiated their construction; both add unmistakable beauty to riverine landscapes more natural in their absence. Heron Pond is spring-fed too. Its most striking feature in summer is the extent to which broad-leaved pondweed (*Potamogeton natans*) covers the water surface, its floating leaves, like tiles, forming a broken jigsaw of a thousand pieces. In winter, the surface is free of these light-harvesters and looks like its more youthful neighbour, Clearwater Pond. Broad-leaved pondweed, it has been shown in studies in France, has a preference for hard water. On a scale of 1–4, from very soft to very hard (calcium-rich) water, broad-leaved pondweed scores 3.

Three views of Clearwater Pond:
Top: The pond, seen from the greatest distance, is barely visible on the left side of the picture frame.
Middle: The island adds interest – is there a moorhen nest?
Bottom: The foreground shows a dense stand of hemp-agrimony (*Eupatorium cannabinum*).

Plant Diversity in Pond Habitats

Plant pond life divides most easily into two habitats: open water and the shoreline. If we were counting invertebrate pond life, we would have to add bottom muds, the habitat of choice for many families of animals without backbones. Open water plants include submerged species, such as Canadian waterweed (*Elodea canadensis*), and species with floating leaves, such as white water-lily (*Nymphaea alba*). Water depth is a limiting condition in the open water habitat. For example, at Heron Pond, white water-lily grows only in the shallow western end, while broad-leaved pondweed ranges over deeper water.

In many ways, the pond edge is a marsh or a habitat similar to the shallows of a slowly moving river. Water mint (*Mentha aquatica*) is found on the shore of both ponds; soft mud in shallow water favours fool's-water-cress (*Apium nodiflorum*) as well. Some species grow in tussocks, others in dense stands, others singly. The amphibian zone of vegetation, the shore provides habitat for the greatest variety of pond-associated species.

A grey heron (*Ardea cinerea*) stood boldly in open sunlight near the pond edge the day of our first visit; but often, he hunts standing motionless in the tall grasses, waiting for a frog or a fish to come within range of his long sharp beak. Rising into the air, the wings spread out like a bedsheet of feathers, the neck is not fully extended but forms a shape like the bend in a pipe, and the long legs trail behind.

Top: Heron Pond in summer. **Bottom:** Heron Pond in winter, with ice covering the surface.

HAZEL TERRACE WOOD

HAZEL (*Corylus avellana*) is usually a shrub (1–6 m), but in the wildwood of post-glacial England it was more often a tree. Aspen, birch and pine were the earliest colonists of the newly-exposed post-glacial terrain; hazel came along shortly thereafter. Grey willow (*Salix cinerea*) and hazel occur more commonly than any other woody plant in the upper course of the Swere, especially above Swerford, where the steep hills beside the river compress the bottomland to a valley not wider than 10–15 m on each side, and moisture is held in the wood by the run-off of springs from the hillslopes.

Hazel is an under-exploited natural resource, a pensioner from the farm economy known to Thomas Hardy. In Wessex days, men coppiced hazel every seven to ten years, cleared the underbrush, made hurdles, barrel hoops and spars for thatching. Bean poles may still be cut for the vegetable garden, but bamboo is more often available. Hazelnuts were an essential part of the diet of prehistoric people and are still gathered by country foragers, but today they mainly feed woodpeckers and wood mice (*Apodemus sylvaticus*).

Marsh-marigold (*Caltha palustris*) grows in the shallow rills that cross the woodland floor from springs on the northern edge; there were 25 flowering plants in one rill. Bluebells (*Hyacinthoides non-scripta*) and dog's mercury (*Mercurialis perennis*), species that are associated with ancient woodland, are not plentiful; they grow at the northern edge where the land rises, and away from the wetter ground to the south. The flowers of marsh-marigold, which are to our eyes uniformly yellow, look very different to a bee; we see no guidelines to pollen and nectar but, in the eye of a bee, the centre will appear almost black and the edges 'bee purple'.

Both photographs show the shrubby habit of growth of hazel (*Corylus avellana*), with many stems arising from its base. An attractive feature of hazel is that it blooms in late winter, before the leaves have opened. The anthers of the male catkins are bright yellow, giving the wood and roadside a dash of colour before the blooming of the first spring flowers.

Hazel Terrace Wood is about 10 m wide, fairly flat, extending from the base of the SSSI on its north side to the river's edge. Hazel is plentiful near the river's edge; common hawthorn (*Crataegus monogyna*) is most abundant on the outer edge of the wood. Tall trees – ash (*Fraxinus excelsior*) and English oak (*Quercus robur*) – are few, and the canopy is often open, yielding sunlight for common nettle (*Urtica dioica*) and meadowsweet (*Filipendula ulmaria*). Crack-willows (*Salix fragilis*), with their lower limbs spread parallel to the ground at eye level, blanketed in moss and lichen, are the most common trees of the wood. One splendid wayfaring-tree (*Viburnum lantana*) counteracts the regret that there is little variety in woody species.

Moss is abundant on crack-willow and elder limbs; in the herb storey (a herb is any seed-bearing plant which does not have a woody stem and dies down to the ground after flowering), dog's mercury (*Mercurialis perennis*) is common, but lords-and-ladies (*Arum maculatum*) is sparsely represented. Two rills, each arising from a spring, cross the terrace, one joining the other. In their wet black soils, marsh-marigold (*Caltha palustris*) luxuriates; 25 plants were blooming, and 18 others were counted along the main rill on 15 April 2003. On another visit, more were found in the leaf-covered firmer muds of the terrace, away from the rivulets. Water figwort (*Scrophularia auriculata*) is associated with marsh-marigold in the rill muds.

Dog's mercury occurs only in patches; it is more abundant on the upslope of the northern edge than anywhere in the wide middle section of the terrace. More abundant is meadowsweet, associated with wood dock (*Rumex sanguineus*) and common nettle in sunny places, also growing in greater shade and wetter ground. Dog's mercury and bluebell (*Hyacinthoides non-scripta*) occur together on the drier upslope at the margin of the wood.

Tom Chester, of Evenley, identified the lichen taxa of one branch of an elder (*Sambucus nigra*) shrub in Hazel Terrace Wood. The main covering is *Parmelia sulcata*; additionally there were *Hypogymnia physodes*, *Lepraria incana*, the shiny metallic-brown *Melanelia fuliginosa* ssp. *glabratula*, and the apple-green *Flavoparmelia caperata*, 'a clean-air species which is again on the increase'.[18] Hazel Terrace Wood, while really nothing more than a neglected space by the river, with wicker-broom growths of *Corylus avellana*, is however a lichen litmus test for the biotic health of the upper Swere valley.

Hazel (*Corylus avellana*), also called cob-nut; male and female flowers occur separately on the same shrub. In the photograph **above**, yellow male catkins are pendent; in the photograph **below**, the hazel fruits, which are nuts with hard woody shells, occur in clusters of 1–4.

SITE OF SPECIAL SCIENTIFIC INTEREST (SSSI)

SSSIs were designed to preserve a representative series of all 'wildlife and geology rich semi-natural habitats native to Britain'.[19] For example, a wood is cleared and grass planted; but when the grassland is left for native species to flourish, then plant and animal communities are created which differ from more intensively managed pastures. The limestone grassland at Swere Bank is just such a naturally modified man-made habitat. The priority for managers of SSSIs is to know the characteristics of their site and to maintain favourable conservation conditions for them.

From the summit of the SSSI, we can see Clearwater Pond perched above the riverside wood far below, a field of maize on a hill across the river, a buzzard circling nearer and nearer, and woods enshrouding the river on its way to Swerford Park. An SSSI is a formal declaration that a particular habitat – a meadow, a wood, a basaltic outcrop, or, as in this case, a grassy slope – merits protection. It is a judgement of excellence.

Looking toward the summit of the site of special scientific interest at Swere Bank.

Left: The harebell (*Campanula rotundifolia*) is an exquisite flower borne on a slender stem. Only the basal leaves are nearly round, and these wither, usually before flowering, leaving the narrow lance-shaped leaves of the stem to further emphasize the delicacy of the plant. **Right:** Wild thyme (*Thymus polytrichus*).

The species composition of this SSSI, which pleases anyone who walks the meadow, is not a complete novelty; England has many rich meadows, but few in North Oxfordshire, and this is the richest along the River Swere, with 12 species only found here.

Ringlets and Marbled Whites are species of butterflies seen on this steep limestone grassland.

Left: A Marbled White butterfly (*Melanargia galathea*).
Right: A pair of Ringlet butterflies (*Aphantopus hyperantus*).

Wildflowers of the Protected Grassland at Swere Bank

Autumn Gentian (*Gentianella amarella*)*

Bee Orchid (*Ophrys apifera*)*

Bittersweet (*Solanum dulcamara*)

Black Medick (*Medicago lupulina*)

Bladder Campion (*Silene vulgaris*)

Burnet-saxifrage (*Pimpinella saxifraga*)

Clustered Bellflower (*Campanula glomerata*)*

Cock's-foot (*Dactylis glomerata*)

Common Bird's-foot-trefoil (*Lotus corniculatus*)

Common Centaury (*Centaurium erythraea*)

Common Hawthorn (*Crataegus monogyna*)

Common Knapweed (*Centaurea nigra*)

Common Milkwort (*Polygala vulgaris*)

Common Ragwort (*Senecio jacobaea*)

Common Restharrow (*Ononis repens*)*

Common Rock-rose
  (*Helianthemum nummularium*)*

Common Spotted-orchid (*Dactylorhiza fuchsii*)

Cowslip (*Primula veris*)

Creeping Buttercup (*Ranunculus repens*)

Creeping Cinquefoil (*Potentilla reptans*)

Creeping Thistle (*Cirsium arvense*)

Crested Dog's-tail (*Cynosurus cristatus*)

Daisy (*Bellis perennis*)

Devil's-bit Scabious (*Succisa pratensis*)

Dog-rose (*Rosa canina*)

Dropwort (*Filipendula vulgaris*)

Dwarf Thistle (*Cirsium acaule*)

Eyebright (*Euphrasia nemorosa*)*

Fairy Flax (*Linum catharticum*)*

False Oat-grass (*Arrhenatherum elatius*)

Field Bindweed (*Convolvulus arvensis*)

Field Forget-me-not (*Myosotis arvensis*)

Field Scabious (*Knautia arvensis*)

Germander Speedwell (*Veronica chamaedrys*)

Glaucous Sedge (*Carex flacca*)

Goat's-beard (*Tragopogon pratensis*)

Greater Knapweed (*Centaurea scabiosa*)

Greater Plantain (*Plantago major*)

Hairy Violet (*Viola hirta*)

Harebell (*Campanula rotundifolia*)

Hawkweed Oxtongue (*Picris hieracioides*)*

Hoary Plantain (*Plantago media*)

Horseshoe-vetch (*Hippocrepis comosa*)*

Kidney Vetch (*Anthyllis vulneraria*)*

Lady's Bedstraw (*Galium verum*)

Meadow Buttercup (*Ranunculus acris*)

Meadowsweet (*Filipendula ulmaria*)

Meadow Vetchling (*Lathyrus pratensis*)

Mouse-ear-hawkweed (*Pilosella officinarum*)

Oxeye Daisy (*Leucanthemum vulgare*)

Perforated St John's-wort
  (*Hypericum perforatum*)

Quaking-grass (*Briza media*)

Red Clover (*Trifolium pratense*)

Ribwort Plantain (*Plantago lanceolata*)

Rough Hawkbit (*Leontodon hispidus*)

Sainfoin (*Onobrychis viciifolia*)*

Salad Burnet (*Sanguisorba minor* ssp. *minor*)

Selfheal (*Prunella vulgaris*)

Small Scabious (*Scabiosa columbaria*)

Spear Thistle (*Cirsium vulgare*)

Sweet Vernal-grass (*Anthoxanthum odoratum*)

Tor-grass (*Brachypodium pinnatum*)

Tufted Hair-grass (*Deschampsia cespitosa*)

Tufted Vetch (*Vicia cracca*)

White Clover (*Trifolium repens*)

Wild Thyme (*Thymus polytrichus*)*

Woolly Thistle (*Cirsium eriophorum*)

Yarrow (*Achillea millefolium*)

Yellow Oat-grass (*Trisetum flavescens*)

Yellow-rattle (*Rhinanthus minor*)

Yorkshire-fog (*Holcus lanatus*)

*Plants only found on this site.

Top left: Woolly thistle (*Cirsium eriophorum*). **Top right:** Field scabious (*Knautia arvensis*).
Bottom left: Common centaury (*Centaurium erythraea*). **Bottom right:** Clustered bellflower (*Campanula glomerata*). Notice the hoverfly on the *Cirsium*. Apparently stationary in mid-air for several seconds, hoverflies look like small wasps, and perhaps they wish to do so, but, unlike wasps, they have only one pair of wings and the waist is not pinched.

A FLOODPLAIN WOOD

LONG BEFORE the sixteenth century, the river valleys and hills would have been wooded, but the very fertility of the soils militated against preserving the forests, except a copse to serve local needs (fuel, hurdles, tools). Today, woodland borders the Swere in narrow strips and isolated patches, more in the upper course than elsewhere.

A floodplain is 'alluviated land of minor relief traversed by a river channel'.[20] The Swere meanders freely the length of a floodplain wood, about 1 ha in area, before entering Swerford Park, just east of the SSSI. Shallow rills, arising from springs at the base of the steep hill on its northern edge, cross the wood, providing habitat for marsh-marigold (*Caltha palustris*). The moist and shaded wood is habitat for rare to uncommon species in Oxfordshire: common twayblade (*Listera ovata*), herb-Paris (*Paris quadrifolia*), meadow saffron (*Colchicum autumnale*), and sanicle (*Sanicula europaea*). Herb-Paris and sanicle also grow in Swere Bank Wood, upstream from the SSSI.

Meadow saffron (*Colchicum autumnale*). This beauty is leafless at flowering, and looks like crocus; the plant stores food in its corm during the summer to support the blossom of autumn. Meadow saffron is extremely rare along the Swere, occurring only at two locations in the upper course.

Left: A shallow rill crossing the floodplain wood. **Right:** The River Swere at the site of its measurement for the figure below. In a scene characteristic of the upper course, the Swere passes by over a stony bottom.

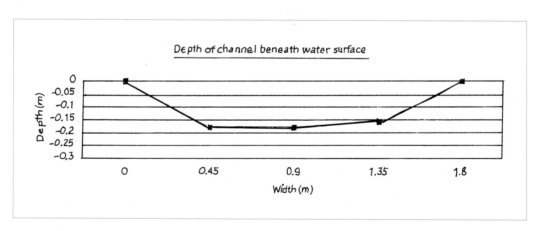

River depth and width of the Swere (it is very shallow and narrow) was measured in February 2003 by master's degree students working under Dr Heather Viles and with Professor Andrew Goudie from the School of Geography, University of Oxford.

Herbaceous and Woody Plants in the Hook Norton Floodplain Wood

Ash (*Fraxinus excelsior*)

Bearded Couch (*Elymus caninus*)

Blackberry (*Rubus fruticosus*)

Black-Italian Poplar (*Populus* 'Serotina')

Blackthorn (*Prunus spinosa*)

Bluebell (*Hyacinthoides non-scripta*)

Bog Stitchwort (*Stellaria uliginosa*)

Broad-leaved Dock (*Rumex obtusifolius*)

Brooklime (*Veronica beccabunga*)

Buckthorn (*Rhamnus cathartica*)

Bugle (*Ajuga reptans*)

Cleavers (*Galium aparine*)

Common Nettle (*Urtica dioica*)

Common Twayblade (*Listera ovata*)

Cow Parsley (*Anthriscus sylvestris*)

Crack-willow (*Salix fragilis*)

Cuckooflower (*Cardamine pratensis*)

Dog's Mercury (*Mercurialis perennis*)

Dog-rose (*Rosa canina*)

Dogwood (*Cornus sanguinea*)

Enchanter's Nightshade (*Circaea lutetiana*)

False Brome (*Brachypodium sylvaticum*)

Field-rose (*Rosa arvensis*)

Giant Fescue (*Festuca gigantea*)

Goldilocks Buttercup (*Ranunculus auricomus*)

Great Willowherb (*Epilobium hirsutum*)

Guelder-rose (*Viburnum opulus*)

Hairy-brome (*Bromopsis ramosa*)

Hard Rush (*Juncus inflexus*)

Hazel (*Corylus avellana*)

Hedge Woundwort (*Stachys sylvatica*)

Herb-Paris (*Paris quadrifolia*)

Herb-Robert (*Geranium robertianum*)

Ivy (*Hedera helix*)

Lesser Burdock (*Arctium minus*)

Lesser Celandine (*Ranunculus ficaria*)

Lesser Pond-sedge (*Carex acutiformis*)

Lords-and-Ladies (*Arum maculatum*)

Male-fern (*Dryopteris filix-mas*)

Marsh-marigold (*Caltha palustris*)

Marsh Thistle (*Cirsium palustre*)

Meadow Saffron (*Colchicum autumnale*)

Meadowsweet (*Filipendula ulmaria*)

Polypody (*Polypodium vulgare*)

Red Campion (*Silene dioica*)

Red Currant (*Ribes rubrum*)

Sanicle (*Sanicula europaea*)

Soft-rush (*Juncus effusus*)

Sweet Violet (*Viola odorata*)

Three-nerved Sandwort (*Moehringia trinervia*)

Tufted Hair-grass (*Deschampsia cespitosa*)

Water-cress (*Rorippa nasturtium-aquatica*)

Water Figwort (*Scrophularia auriculata*)

Water Mint (*Mentha aquatica*)

Wayfaring-tree (*Viburnum lantana*)

Wild Angelica (*Angelica sylvestris*)

Wood Avens (*Geum urbanum*)

Wood Dock (*Rumex sanguineus*)

Wood-sedge (*Carex sylvatica*)

Yellow Archangel (*Lamiastrum galeobdolon*)

While this is a tiny fragment of woodland, it is the only wild floodplain wood along the entire length of the Swere and of interest to the naturalist. In a report of 12 'ancient woodland' indicator species, made by Camilla Lambrick in 2002 for County Wildlife Sites, we saw those marked below with an asterisk, but did not see bearded couch (*Elymus caninus*), giant fescue (*Festuca gigantea*), polypody (*Polypodium vulgare*), three-nerved sandwort (*Moehringia trinervia*) and wood-sedge (*Carex sylvatica*).[21]

The ground flora is a mosaic of habitats grading from wet, with marsh-marigold, to moist, with tufted hair-grass (*Deschampsia cespitosa*), locally dominant, to dry ground, with bugle (*Ajuga reptans*) and red campion (*Silene dioica*), and is rich with bog stitchwort (*Stellaria uliginosa*), cuckooflower (*Cardamine pratensis*) and yellow archangel (*Lamiastrum galeobdolon*)*. Dog's mercury (*Mercurialis perennis*), ivy (*Hedera helix*) and moss dominate; bluebell (*Hyacinthoides non-scripta*)*, Goldilocks buttercup (*Ranunculus auricomus*) and lesser celandine (*R. ficaria*) add variety and colour.

In the shrub storey, blackthorn (*Prunus spinosa*) is common at the western end, and there are buckthorn (*Rhamnus cathartica*), dogwood (*Cornus sanguinea*), field-rose (*Rosa arvensis*)*, guelder-rose (*Viburnum opulus*)*, red currant (*Ribes rubrum*)* and wayfaring-tree (*Viburnum lantana*). Ash (*Fraxinus excelsior*), tall and spindly, is the dominant tree at the western end and black-Italian poplar (*Populus* 'Serotina'), a cross of *P. nigra* with *P. deltoides*, at the eastern end. With flattened petioles, the poplar's blades flutter in the breeze, amplifying the autumn wind.

On the ground in the wetter wood, there are hairy-brome (*Bromopsis ramosa*)*, lesser pond-sedge (*Carex acutiformis*), male-fern (*Dryopteris filix-mas*), meadowsweet (*Filipendula ulmaria*), soft-rush (*Juncus effusus*), sweet violet (*Viola odorata*)*, water mint (*Mentha aquatica*), wild angelica (*Angelica sylvestris*) and wood dock (*Rumex sanguineus*). By the river edge, where there is extra moisture as well as more sunlight, there are brooklime (*Veronica beccabunga*), hard rush (*Juncus inflexus*), lesser pond-sedge, marsh thistle (*Cirsium palustre*), soft-rush, water-cress (*Rorippa nasturtium-aquaticum*), water figwort (*Scrophularia auriculata*) and water mint.

Left: Herb-Paris (*Paris quadrifolia*) **Right:** Red campion (*Silene dioica*)

CHURCH MARSH, SWERFORD

A SPARROWHAWK flying low over a distant hedge introduces Church Marsh, the first site of botanical interest below Floodplain Wood. The marsh lies at the bottom of a hill above which the earthwork remains of a motte and bailey castle form an impressive archaeological site, one from which a wide and sweeping view of the pressing hills is possible. The fortress was probably used before the Norman Conquest, but Swerford – a village of great tranquility and beauty – is so little populated, and at peace with all its neighbours, that it is difficult to imagine a castle was ever necessary. A small herd of Friesian dairy cattle graze the grassy banks rising from the wet bottomland to the churchyard gate.

Church Marsh is at the lowest elevation in the valley, occupying the flooded sides of a feeble stream, the stream which once was the River Swere. But long ago the river was given a new channel, man-made with fortifying banks and elevated above the valley floor. The river was harnessed before 1066 to increase the flow to the corn-mill owned by Osney Abbey, Oxford. While the mill wheel no longer turns, the leat remains and the river continues to travel in its elevated channel. We then realized that the marsh that lies below the river level on its south side, is the River Swere – water following the course it took before the main volume was diverted to form the leat. The countryside is a series of puzzles and the pleasure of walking is the chance to think about them.

In the pellucid water of the shallow stream there was, in open sunlight, a white-clawed crayfish (*Austropotamobius pallipes*) swimming among its gravels, as shown in the photographs in the next chapter. This is the native crayfish. Two springs arise on a grassy slope, towards the eastern end of the field, and enrich the stream before it rejoins the river which has been separated from it. The vegetation of the trampled wet muds along the side of the river-stream is a sedge and rush marsh. By late winter, the sedges have been nibbled and gnawed, evenly cut, the way parkland trees are pruned to a browse line.

Wherever woody plants are self-sown along a leat bank in this part of Oxfordshire, one is sure to find ash (*Fraxinus excelsior*), common hawthorn (*Crataegus monogyna*), pollarded crack-willow (*Salix fragilis*), hazel (*Corylus avellana*), holly (*Ilex aquifolium*) and sycamore (*Acer pseudoplatanus*). By the leat, a miniature wet wood has formed, rich with ferns – broad buckler-fern (*Dryopteris dilatata*), male-fern (*D. filix-mas*) and polypody (*Polypodium vulgare*) – and a large stand of great horsetail (*Equisetum telmateia*).

Cattle grazing and drinking by the side of the stream have puddled the earth, and forced mud to rise up in the shape of tussocks (see the photograph opposite). Bristle club-rush (*Isolepis setacea*), 'scarce' in the county, reported from only 16 of 596 tetrads (a tetrad = 2 km square) in *The Flora of Oxfordshire*,[22] grows on these tussocks. A complete list of the herbaceous species of the stream edge and trampled muds will be of interest, for this is a habitat that could change; indeed, the river could take its old course, and flow through the lowest level of the valley once again.

Species of the Stream Edge and Trampled Muds of Church Marsh

Bog Stitchwort (*Stellaria uliginosa*)
Bristle Club-rush (*Isolepis setacea*)
Brooklime (*Veronica beccabunga*)
Common Spike-rush (*Eleocharis palustris*)
Fool's-water-cress (*Apium nodiflorum*)
Greater Bird's-foot-trefoil (*Lotus pedunculatus*)
Greater Pond-sedge (*Carex riparia*)
Hard Rush (*Juncus inflexus*)
Hemp-agrimony (*Eupatorium cannabinum*)
Hoary Willowherb (*Epilobium parviflorum*)
Lesser Celandine (*Ranunculus ficaria*)

Marsh Horsetail (*Equisetum palustre*)
Marsh Thistle (*Cirsium palustre*)
Meadowsweet (*Filipendula ulmaria*)
Ragged-Robin (*Lychnis flos-cuculi*)
Square-stalked St John's-wort
  (*Hypericum tetrapterum*)
Water-cress (*Rorippa nasturtium-aquaticum*)
Water Figwort (*Scrophularia auriculata*)
Water Forget-me-not (*Myosotis scorpioides*)
Water Mint (*Mentha aquatica*)
Wavy Bitter-cress (*Cardamine flexuosa*)

Trampled muds and mud tussocks in Church Marsh, Swerford.

CRAYFISH AND OTHER INVERTEBRATES

THE RIVER is a varying mix of chemical elements in solution, as well as a conduit for leaves, twigs, pollen, insect and other animal bodies, decomposing and adding organic molecules to the cocktail. Like any biological environment, the river is a combination of habitats, principally stratified from the water surface to the bottom muds. There are nymphs and larvae of various insects between and under pebbles and gravel, and attached to the underside of water-lily leaves. It is reassuring to know that the Swere's invertebrate life, recently inventoried by Ben McFarland of the Environment Agency, has been found flourishing, a sign of river health.

At the bottom of the food chain are the bacterial and fungal decomposers feeding on the drift of leaves and the 'living soil' splashed into the river from the land. Fishermen are more likely to know stoneflies (Plecoptera) and many mayflies (Ephemoptera), their larvae harvesting smaller creatures rushing by in the torrent of passing water. Both groups are well-represented in the Swere. Searching for its meal and seeking concealment in shadowy places is the native crayfish.

White-clawed crayfish (*Austropotamobius pallipes*): notice how much more clearly the crayfish in the right photograph is speckled, and more sharply coloured, than the one on the left, but they are the same individual, the photograph taken at different moments. On the left, he is swimming along quite merrily, with his body fully extended. Then, in the right photograph, he, or she, has tucked the abdominal segments under and is ready to speed away backwards. Small and medium stones, probably coated with tufa, to which sediments are adhering, are clearly visible in the left photograph, and give the crayfish places to hide and to hunt.

In all its anatomical structures, the crayfish is like the lobster, with large pincers a third the length of its body. Only one species of crayfish is native to the British Isles, the white-clawed crayfish (*Austropotamobius pallipes*); it is one of the UK's largest mobile freshwater invertebrates, growing up to 25 cm in length. It is usually found in well-oxygenated hard-water where the water is shallow but fast-flowing, in the upper course of the Swere. In 1999, when Keith Loban, of South Newington, set about repairing the sluice gate at the South Newington mill, he found 57 white-clawed crayfish, which the Environment Agency, in Wallingford, took away and relocated in the river.

Because the crayfish is susceptible to lowered levels of oxygen, its presence in reasonable numbers is an indication that the Swere, which is a calcareous stream, has a clean bill of health. A deficiency of calcium, as in an acid stream, would prevent the formation of the animal's hard exoskeleton. Julia Warnford-Davis, of South Newington, has reported seeing other invertebrates: dragonfly and damselfly (Odonata) larvae, caddisflies (Trichoptera), mayflies and stoneflies. Adult mayflies live only a few days, and the family is called Ephemoptera for that reason, but the nymphs live for two to three years in water.

Caddisfly larvae are found beneath the flat stones that lie in the river on either side of Adderbury Bridge. Here the river is shallow and fast moving. The particular species that lives at this location builds a case of small fragments of stone. As water passes through these cases, the larvae feed on the smaller animals that pass by. A related species of caddisfly constructs a net of minute silken threads, usually strung between two sticks or logs.

Left: Adult stonefly (Plecoptera). **Centre:** Adult mayfly (Ephemoptera). **Right:** Adult caddisfly (Trichoptera).[23] Species of each of these groups live in the Swere. Mayflies are best known, probably because the delicate lacing of their wings is so attractive. Characteristic too is the upswung abdomen and the trailing ovipositor. Mayflies hatch in hordes, cloud a summer's evening, and lay their eggs in gelatinous masses attached to aquatic plants. Caddisflies are moth-like insects having wings covered with hairs rather than scales. The nymphs of many caddisfly species build portable cases in which they pass the days and months of their young years. The cases may identify the species; those living within the shadow of Adderbury Bridge, for example, build straight tubular cases dotted with small pieces of gravel, giving the impression of tile work without grouting.

PART I · THE UPPER COURSE OF THE RIVER

'After mating in the autumn, the female crayfish (not a fish!) lays about 100 eggs which she carries under her abdomen until they hatch the following spring.'[24] When engaged in its ordinary pursuits – scavenging, eating vegetation, or hunting small prey – the crayfish walks forward slowly and jerkily but, if disturbed, it shoots backwards, out of harm's way, by contracting its abdominal muscles. Both photographs on page 48 are of the same crayfish, seen in the river where it is shallow and flows through Church Marsh below Swerford village. Since the crayfish is mainly nocturnal, and prefers living inconspicuously below or behind rocks and vegetation, the one in the river at Church Marsh seems to have decided he has nothing to fear from heron or naturalist, and moves along at midday in clear water.

The crayfish is protected under Schedule 5 of the 1981 Wildlife and Countryside Act: the animal must not be taken from the wild or sold. Before 1980, local children caught crayfish frequently; but it is not thought that their decline in numbers was due to Tom Sawyer's summer depredations. Disease has been a factor. The disease which threatens them most is 'crayfish plague', a fungal disease carried and spread by the invasive signal crayfish (*Pacifastacus leniusculus*). By preventing its further introduction, we can reduce the risk to our native populations. Surprisingly, and despite competition, there have been cases of natives and signals living side by side.

Invertebrate life is more attractive to children than adults. Certainly crayfish arouse the hunter in country boys and girls. River health, including invertebrate life, is regularly monitored by the Environment Agency; but they cannot observe the goings on in a small river as often as they would like to do. Perhaps there should be an 'all Swere committee' making regular inspections of caddisfly larvae and white-clawed crayfish populations. With luck, one day the white-clawed crayfish will be common enough to invite the village children to try their patience as hunters … with cameras.

Left: To anyone wanting to look for the nymphs of aquatic species (the adults of which species all have aerial lives!), east of the South Newington ford is an ideal reach of river: gravelly and fast flowing. This photograph is on the upper Swere at Slinket Wood.

INTRODUCING
MARSHES

A S A GENERAL RULE, marshes are a nuisance. They tempt the farmer to install expensive drains in the hope of increasing yields. Resisting this impulse, the farmer lets the land lie fallow, conceding to nature the defeat or delay of his ambitions. Marshes are still the breeding ground of noxious insects, especially mosquitoes, but more in Central America than in the Swere valley. In any war, marshes are an impediment to movement:

'My Lord, the enemy is past the marsh.'

from *Richard III*

Peat Marsh, west of South Newington.

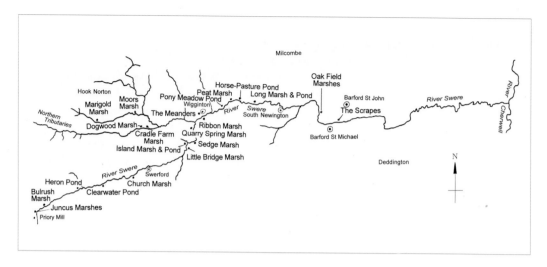

Map of the Swere valley showing the principal marshes along the river course.

In the machine age, the tractor can go round the marsh, but Stephenson built part of the Liverpool to Manchester Railway over a peat bog, at great cost. On the other hand, marshes are prized by naturalists. One of the earliest of these, in North America, was Henry David Thoreau, who lived a life of intense nonconformity, and gave this expression to a defence of bogs: 'Hope and the future for me are not in lawns and cultivated fields, but in the impervious and quaking swamps.'[25] No other habitat along the River Swere is so munificent in adding a bounty of wildflower species to the landscape, from ragged-Robin to wild angelica.

Some authors reserve the word 'swamp' for wetland formations with tall herbaceous species such as bulrush or reed canary-grass, but the more common use of 'swamp' is for a wetland formation with trees. Dismal Swamp, Virginia, USA, for example, is such a place; vast acres of the Canadian landscape, above the Great Lakes, are boreal swamp forest with black spruce, larch trees and moose. Swere marshes are varied; they have rushes and reeds, sedges and bulrushes, but no trees, and we have twice seen great snipe (*Gallinago media*) in Peat Marsh, near South Newington.

Peat Marsh, small, discrete, spring-fed and dominated by lesser pond-sedge (*Carex acutiformis*) is a good example – and representative – of Swere marshes. The photograph opposite of the marsh shows a central space, uniform in colour, dominated by sedge; rush plants, widely spaced, dot the ground beyond the central zone. Here sedge plants are decaying to produce peat, and the ground quakes when one treads on them.

As in other sedge marshes, the greatest richness of associated herbaceous species in Peat Marsh is towards the outer perimeter of the marsh. Common marsh species are listed in Appendix I, but it is worth mentioning that Peat Marsh, like almost every Swere marsh, has one or more rare to uncommon species in the valley. Marsh arrowgrass (*Triglochin palustre*), which grows here, is one of the rarest plants in the Swere system of habitats. This is a pleasure of marshes: they are a man in plain dress who in conversation has many parts!

Marshes vary by size, shape and species composition. The marsh, as an extreme environment for terrestrial plant life, lends itself to dominance by one or other of the few species that can exploit it. Along the Swere there are sedge, reed, rush, meadowsweet and bulrush marshes; in each kind, one species is dominant. While little space is available for any other species in the marsh centre, a marsh may provide habitat for species that occur nowhere else in the area. If the Swere valley were deprived of its marshes, at least 20 different kinds of plants would vanish from its landscapes.

Dense riverside stands of reed sweet-grass (*Glyceria maxima*) are classified as a type of marsh by professional botanists. The lower photograph opposite shows the Swere nearly idle in midsummer, the right bank dominated by reed sweet-grass.

One would guess that the size and shape of a marsh are related to the water-table. Several marshes are small ovals and, in all cases, the shape is the result of an excavation, the marsh being the successor to a pond. We know this is true of two marshes at the head of the river, and of The Scrapes in Barford St Michael, as well as others. The zonation of plant species tends to create – or impose on the topography – a regularity in shape that is pleasing to the eye. Quarry Spring Marsh is an example of this regularity. At the other extreme is the field or rush marsh, in which plants colonize wet places in meadows and fields ploughed for arable crops, the whole marsh seeming to have no shape or boundary.

Rush marshes are *Juncus*-dotted wet grasslands; their principal component species, either hard rush (*Juncus inflexus*) or soft-rush (*J. effusus*), occur at a greater distance from one another, like the English on a beach, than sedge plants, which are more Italian, thriving on proximity and congestion. There are two rush marshes: one along the upper course of the Swere above Heron Pond, called Juncus Marshes, the other in the middle course of the river, called Oak Field Marshes. Overall, in woods, marshes and pond edges there are more species of sedge than of rush. Sedges have more successfully adapted to woodland habitats: there is wood-sedge (*Carex sylvatica*) but no '*Juncus sylvatica*'. In Swere wetlands, rushes (and hard rush more than soft-rush) occupy more sites than wetland sedges.

Top: Sneezewort (*Achillea ptarmica*). A perennial herb with a creeping rootstock, sneezewort is one of the rarest species of flowering plants occurring at only 1 of 29 marsh/pond sites along the River Swere and its northern tributary.

Bottom: Reed sweet-grass (*Glyceria maxima*). East of Little Barford Mill, white clouds are reflected in the river where one yellow water-lily (*Nuphar lutea*) is about to bloom. Sheep and cattle graze far from the rich stands of reed sweet-grass and, in the distance, the land rises towards the ridge of the Hempton Road, Deddington.

Confusing, but not impossible to distinguish, soft-rush (*Juncus effusus*) (**right**) is a lighter green and has more yellow; hard rush (*J. inflexus*) (**left**) is a darker green and shows a more grey-green cast from a distance. Feeling the stems, hard rush has prominent ridges; soft-rush is smooth. The very difficulty of knowing the difference between plants so common is a challenge to the country walker and one to be met and won.

Between these two forms – the small oval and the large field marsh – is a marsh taking the linear shape of an old river channel. In each case, the greater flow of water has been captured, long ago, by a mill leat. Ribbon Marsh, near Wigginton, bends and curves in the old river's channel, and Long Marsh and Pond, which is the gold medallist of Swere marshes, follows the shape of the old channel in which spring water collects from the neighbouring steep grassy slope.

The most obvious variation in Swere marshes is size. Little Bridge Marsh is tiny (*ca* 5 m x 5 m); some marshes are even smaller – Mint Marsh, for example. In some cases, a small marsh is no more than the muddy edge of a spring-fed pond. This is true of Cow Pond Marsh, Horse-Pasture Marsh and Pony Meadow Marsh, or the edge of a stream or watery gulley – for example, Church Marsh.

Small marshes have greater mixtures of herbaceous plant species in their central places, and are therefore richer than large marshes which tend to be dominated by sedge, as are Island Marsh and Pond and Long Marsh and Pond, or by rush, like Oak Field Marshes. In sedge marshes, species diversity is greatest at the edge, for, with the drop in surface water, the sedges give way. This is true at Long Marsh, where the edge is very rich, or in places where the congestion of greater pond-sedge (*Carex riparia*) has relented. The '*Carex riparia* swamp', as it is called, of which the marsh at Island Marsh and Pond is a good example, is nearly a single species stand throughout.[26]

While some sedge marshes are dominated by a single species – lesser pond-sedge at Peat Marsh, for example – others are not. A marsh may have a strong representation of sedge, as Mare's-tail Marsh and Pond does, but not be dominated by it. On the other hand, a marsh may be dominated by a collection of sedge species, not just one. At Long Marsh, for example,

Tall weeping plants – greater pond-sedge (*Carex riparia*) – stand at the edge of Island Marsh and Pond, then extend for a great distance away from it. Less tousled is common bulrush (*Typha latifolia*) rising above the sedge. The pond is congested with curly waterweed (*Lagarosiphon major*) below the water surface, and fringed water-lily (*Nymphoides peltata*), which is the most abundant of the floating leaves; there are a few larger oval leaves of white water-lily (*Nymphaea alba*).

slender tufted-sedge (*Carex acuta*) is locally dominant; greater pond-sedge occurs plentifully in an outer zone, and is, as well, interspersed with lesser pond-sedge, with the result that Long Marsh is a multiple-sedge marsh. Cradle Farm Marsh, east of Hook Norton on the northern tributary of the Swere, is the largest marsh, and has the largest extent of sedge in the Swere system.

Meadowsweet (*Filipendula ulmaria*) occurs widely in a range of wetland habitats, from pond edge to wet meadow, but it will not, as branched bur-reed (*Sparganium erectum*) does, stand with its feet covered by a flowing river. Meadowsweet marshes are congested too, but they are drier than sedge marshes and, in the succession from pond to dry land, they are a later stage. The largest stand of meadowsweet, where wild angelica (*Angelica sylvestris*) is an abundant associate, is in a long narrow valley north of the river Swere in Great Rollright parish. Meadowsweet dominates Floodplain Marsh, below the South Newington bridge on the Banbury Road; again, wild angelica is a plentiful associate with great willowherb (*Epilobium hirsutum*).

Species Occurrence

Thirty-five families of flowering plants are represented at 29 sites. The sedge family (Cyperaceae) has the greatest number of species – 17; greater pond-sedge is the most common sedge. Three families have 7 species each: Juncaceae, Lamiaceae and Poaceae. Fifty-eight species are found in less than 10% of sites.

The species occurring most often in Swere River valley wetlands are meadowsweet, reed canary-grass (*Phalaris arundinacea*), tufted hair-grass (*Deschampsia cespitosa*) and wild angelica; water mint (*Mentha aquatica*) occurs at a high percentage of sites as well.

Above: A sedge marsh, dominated by lesser pond-sedge (*Carex acutiformis*), which we are calling Cradle Farm Marsh, the largest anywhere along the Swere.

Left: The advantage meadowsweet (*Filipendula ulmaria*) has over sedge and rush, plants that in their variety and difficulty of identification delight botanists, is that it is pretty. Meadowsweet is more universal in habitat preference: it will thrive in roadside and hedgerow ditches, wet woods and meadows, and alongside the Swere and other rivers. Meadowsweet is a perennial herb, which is why, when it gains a foothold, it more easily retains it and expands its populations to the very limit of the space that suits it.

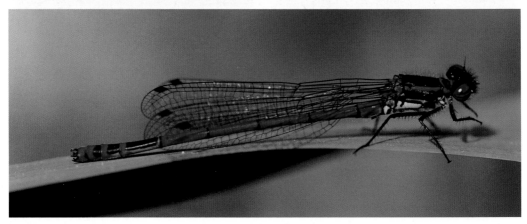

Top left: Purple-loosestrife (*Lythrum salicaria*), present in 13 of 29 marsh sites; for comparison, the most frequently occurring wetland species is meadowsweet (*Filipendula ulmaria*), occurring at 24 of 29 sites. Not greatly less frequent than *Lythrum* is yellow iris (*Iris pseudacorus*), present at 12 sites. **Top right:** Wild angelica (*Angelica sylvestris*) in winter. An umbel is a group of flowers whose stems, or pedicels, all arise from the top of the main stem. Wild angelica occurs at 19 of 29 wetland sites. **Bottom:** A Large Red Damselfly (*Pyrrhosoma nymphula*), a species found occasionally in the marshes along the middle course of the River Swere. This is a male; the female is a little larger and has distinct yellow rings at each section of her abdomen.

Four parishes, from Swerford to Milcombe, are marsh-rich. Deddington, in the lower course of the river, where the valley has widened and therefore spring-holding hills have receded, is marsh-poor.

Marshes and Ponds of the River Swere

Parish	Marshes	Ponds	Pond/Marsh
Over Norton	0	3	1
Great Rollright	1	1	0
Little Tew	0	1	0
Swerford	3	1	1
Hook Norton	5	1	0
Wigginton	4	0	0
Milcombe	1	2	1
Bloxham	1	0	0
South Newington	1	0	0
Barford	2	1	0
Deddington	0	0	0
TOTALS	**18**	**10**	**3**

Musk-mallow (*Malva moschata*) in a hedgebank by the river, near Peat Marsh. More a perennial herb of grassy places, pastures and hedgebanks, this mallow added a bright rosy colour to the sombre browns and greens of the marsh and meadow.

Top: Church Marsh, Swerford. The characteristically serpentine branch of an English oak (*Quercus robur*), the bark lit by winter light, extends over the higher bank of the marsh and frames the picture. **Bottom:** Pollard crack-willow (*Salix fragilis*) trees mark the straight course of the River Swere in the wide valley of Barford St Michael; to the right, the Oak Field Marshes begin where the grassland is dotted with rushes.

Top: The pond at the east end of Cradle Farm Marsh is the only wetland site of dogwood, an attractive shrub. Dogwood (*Cornus sanguinea*) is not a wetland species; here it probably was planted, or otherwise it colonized islets in the pond and drier species on the pond's margin. Dogwood reminds us of the geology widespread in the Swere drainage basin for it is a woody plant with a preference for calcareous soils.

Bottom: Walkway Marsh. A handsome wooden walkway straddles the marsh where, despite its small size, it is host to many wildflowers, including purple-loosestrife (*Lythrum salicaria*).

LITTLE BRIDGE MARSH

IN THE HISTORY of nations, the Rhine is as effective as the Alps in separating tribes from kingdoms; the limit of the northward ascendancy of the Roman Empire was set by the Danube, but the Swere has no such pretensions. At most, it separates two parishes, Hook Norton from Swerford. Little Bridge Marsh is a postage stamp marsh, but it has an exceptional diversity of herbaceous plants, including common spotted-orchids (*Dactylorhiza fuchsii*), the largest specimen of marsh thistle (*Cirsium palustre*) and the largest stand of common fleabane (*Pulicaria dysenterica*). In this little patch of ground, a handsome bridge of well-cut and sturdy stones joins the two parishes and forms an arched gateway for the river's debut into open sunlight.

Little Bridge Marsh distinguishes itself from all other marshes in one respect: it is not dominated by any of the marshland sovereigns – not by bulrush, meadowsweet, rush or sedge. It is a republic of short and tall, dense and thin, wetland herbaceous species living in an area of about 5 m x 5 m, flowering and fruiting each according to its kind, including: common spotted-orchid, greater bird's-foot-trefoil (*Lotus pedunculatus*), marsh-marigold (*Caltha palustris*), ragged-Robin (*Lychnis flos-cuculi*) and wild angelica (*Angelica sylvestris*) among representative grasses and rushes, listed in the table below. River edge plants, both above and below the bridge, show a similar disposition towards variety. Above the bridge are brooklime (*Veronica beccabunga*), fool's-water-cress (*Apium nodiflorum*), water-cress (*Rorippa nasturtium-aquaticum*), water forget-me-not (*Myosotis scorpioides*) and water mint (*Mentha aquatica*), plants lying on the water gathering the greatest amount of unobstructed sunlight but securely rooted in the gravelly muds of the shoreline. A. R. Clapham *et al.* describe the habit of water-cress as 'procumbent and rooting below then ascending or floating'.[27]

Top right: Little Bridge Marsh. Summer's sunshine plays on the surface of the flowing stream, spread wide in its channel; lichens yellow the grey-black stones of the bridge's graceful arch.

Bottom left: Marsh thistle (*Cirsium palustre*). How erect yet narrow the marsh thistle is: its form alone may be a key to the species. But it has these properties too: the stems are furrowed and continuously spiny-winged, and it likes wet ground.

Bottom right: Common spotted-orchid (*Dactylorhiza fuchsii*). The leaves are marked with spots or blotches which have no known purpose and yet are not disfiguring, for to be an orchid is to be beautiful.

Variation in depth is a feature of the river along its course. The water is always shallow within the precinct of the marsh above the bridge; in August it ranges between 3–4 cm deep, and chatters over the limestone gravels. West of the bridge the river deepens suddenly, and perilously, to about 60 cm in the same month. Downstream from the bridge, the banks are high, compressing the stream and deepening the channel. Bankside plants are different in kind, taller than any of the plants beside the river above the bridge where the shore is a muddy slip and not a high bank. Walking downstream one may see, in order of their appearance: reed sweet-grass (*Glyceria maxima*), water figwort (*Scrophularia auriculata*), jointed rush (*Juncus articulatus*), wild angelica, lesser water-parsnip (*Berula erecta*), branched bur-reed (*Sparganium erectum*), great willowherb (*Epilobium hirsutum*) and hemp-agrimony (*Eupatorium cannabinum*). Species of the marshy shore are: blue water-speedwell (*Veronica anagallis-aquatica*), great willowherb, hemp-agrimony, reed canary-grass (*Phalaris arundinacea*) and reed sweet-grass.

Species of Little Bridge Marsh

Blue Water-speedwell (*Veronica anagallis-aquatica*)
Branched Bur-reed (*Sparganium erectum*)
Brooklime (*Veronica beccabunga*)
Common Bird's-foot-trefoil (*Lotus corniculatus*)
Common Fleabane (*Pulicaria dysenterica*)
Common Spotted-orchid (*Dactylorhiza fuchsii*)
Fool's-water-cress (*Apium nodiflorum*)
Giant Fescue (*Festuca gigantea*)
Great Willowherb (*Epilobium hirsutum*)
Greater Bird's-foot-trefoil (*Lotus pedunculatus*)
Hairy Sedge (*Carex hirta*)
Hard Rush (*Juncus inflexus*)
Hemp-agrimony (*Eupatorium cannabinum*)
Jointed Rush (*Juncus articulatus*)
Lesser Water-parsnip (*Berula erecta*)
Marsh Horsetail (*Equisetum palustre*)

Marsh-marigold (*Caltha palustris*)
Marsh Thistle (*Cirsium palustre*)
Meadowsweet (*Filipendula ulmaria*)
Ragged-Robin (*Lychnis flos-cuculi*)
Red Fescue (*Festuca rubra*)
Reed Canary-grass (*Phalaris arundinacea*)
Reed Sweet-grass (*Glyceria maxima*)
Soft-rush (*Juncus effusus*)
Timothy (*Phleum pratense*)
Tufted Hair-grass (*Deschampsia cespitosa*)
Water-cress (*Rorippa nasturtium-aquaticum*)
Water Figwort (*Scrophularia auriculata*)
Water Forget-me-not (*Myosotis scorpioides*)
Water Mint (*Mentha aquatica*)
Wild Angelica (*Angelica sylvestris*)
Wood Dock (*Rumex sanguineus*)

Top left: Common fleabane (*Pulicaria dysenterica*). This handsome plant is a perennial herb with a woody rootstock; the smell of the plant is said to be unpleasant to fleas. **Top right:** Great willowherb (*Epilobium hirsutum*). Willowherb is a tall perennial herb, its stem rising to 150 cm. It is common in ditches and marsh edges. **Bottom left:** Water forget-me-not (*Myosotis scorpioides*). The flowers are sky-blue; by the water's edge, the stems lean over the shining surface. **Bottom right:** Water mint (*Mentha aquatica*). The stem is square and a little hairy; the leaves are formed in pairs and scented. Use of mint in cooking dates from the Stone Age.

ISLAND MARSH
AND POND

A WOODEN GATE at the east end of Little Bridge Marsh, with the ground swollen beneath it, is slightly ajar. The gate is the entrance to private land, a meadow shaped like the hull of a ship, upswung on the edges and wider than the riverside meadows upstream from here. The long meadow is dominated by meadowsweet (*Filipendula ulmaria*) and abundantly flowered with wild angelica (*Angelica sylvestris*). For the first time, along the river, there is room to graze a small herd, but grass is little used for cattle in fenced spaces as small as this meadow. At the eastern end is Island Marsh and Pond, concealed by a ring of tall plants and lying at the end of a densely vegetated sedge marsh.

Along the eastern edge of the meadow at Island Marsh and Pond, the river breaks free from a managed course, as it did at Church Marsh; here the river meandering is more handsome than ever before. It snuggles at the base of a steep wooded hill – Slinket Wood – with (and this too is a first) a mixture of tall beech and oak trees. Of particular interest is the presence in the river of a tufa dam.

The pond is oblong more than oval, lies north of the river and is spring-fed. Embedded with curly waterweed (*Lagarosiphon major*), the water seems more like a gel than a liquid, and is sullen and dark. Is it a nursery for damselflies? The pond has both alien and native species. Fringed water-lily (*Nymphoides peltata*) and water-soldier (*Stratiotes aloides*) are native to the British Isles but not to Oxfordshire; we venture that white water-lily (*Nymphaea alba*) was planted too. But the vegetation of the pond's edge is a hurly-burly of plants wild and native to the marsh habitat.

All the edges of the island and surrounding pond are dominated by plants that form dense stands. Tallest of these are: branched bur-reed (*Sparganium erectum*), common bulrush (*Typha latifolia*) and common reed (*Phragmites australis*) – 'our tallest native grass'. *Phragmites*, a rhizomatous perennial with annual aerial leaves and flowers, is able to endure prolonged water-logging of its soils. Less tall, but not less dense, is greater pond-sedge (*Carex riparia*), the dominant species of the marsh. Less densely, great willowherb (*Epilobium hirsutum*) crowds the pond edge. Some species, infrequently seen in Oxfordshire, afford special distinction to this site: notably, blunt-flowered rush (*Juncus subnodulosus*) and wood club-rush (*Scirpus sylvaticus*).

Right: Island Marsh and Pond in early spring.

Species of Island Marsh

Blunt-flowered Rush (*Juncus subnodulosus*)

Branched Bur-reed (*Sparganium erectum*)

Common Bulrush (*Typha latifolia*)

Common Marsh-bedstraw (*Galium palustre*)

Common Reed (*Phragmites australis*)

Curly Waterweed (*Lagarosiphon major*)

False Fox-sedge (*Carex otrubae*)

Fringed Water-lily (*Nymphoides peltata*)

Giant Fescue (*Festuca gigantea*)

Great Willowherb (*Epilobium hirsutum*)

Greater Pond-sedge (*Carex riparia*)

Hairy-brome (*Bromopsis ramosa*)

Hedge Woundwort (*Stachys sylvatica*)

Hoary Willowherb (*Epilobium parviflorum*)

Jointed Rush (*Juncus articulatus*)

Marsh Thistle (*Cirsium palustre*)

Meadowsweet (*Filipendula ulmaria*)

Purple-loosestrife (*Lythrum salicaria*)

Reed Sweet-grass (*Glyceria maxima*)

Sharp-flowered Rush (*Juncus acutiflorus*)

Water-soldier (*Stratiotes aloides*)

White Water-lily (*Nymphaea alba*)

Wild Angelica (*Angelica sylvestris*)

Wood Club-rush (*Scirpus sylvaticus*)

Yellow Iris (*Iris pseudacorus*)

Yellow Loosestrife (*Lysimachia vulgaris*)

North of the pond are four rows of young beech (*Fagus sylvatica*) trees, tall enough – nearly 10 m high – to form a closed canopy and cover the ground with leaves so numerous that barely a single herb grows, except bluebells (*Hyacinthoides non-scripta*). The bluebells grow on the eastern edge of the beech wood in the shade of older oak trees; there are also cowslips (*Primula veris*) where the wood faces the pond and marsh, and a field of common nettle (*Urtica dioica*) on the moist ground adjoining the river.

FARMER TUSTIAN'S PASTURES AND A VILLAGE POND

THERE IS NO QUESTION that by application of nitrogen and phosphate, and by the use of herbicides and insecticides, yields of agricultural crops have been greatly increased since the beginning of the twentieth century, increases that could not have been made by any other means. Passing by these fields, in which the absence of zigzagging butterflies, twittering larks and buzzing bees are sights and sounds missed, it is a consolation to the naturalist that the crops achieve a remarkable uniformity in height and volume of yield. The landscape canvas of oilseed-rape and winter wheat is not varied by an adventurous palette. Farmer Tustian's pastures, on the other hand, have a different look, and bid one to visit them.

They lie south of the ridge road running west from Swerford village and joining, at its end, the north-south road connecting the Chipping Norton road to the paved way to Hook Norton. Before reaching the pastures, one's eyes rise northward and down steep fields that run to a wood, cross it, and rise again – the fields of Swerford Park. Some days, one will see a contest of riders in these parkland fields dotted with trees, and with their splendidly managed grassy swards. Farmer Tustian's land is, by comparison, managed with a greater indifference to its appearance. The turf is coarse and many grasses and herbs are self-sown. He manages the land without applying more nitrogen than sheep add to it. As a result there is a greater variety of herbaceous plants and a rough and irregular beauty.

In moist places, where the land has dipped and not been levelled, cuckooflower (*Cardamine pratensis*), lesser celandine (*Ranunculus ficaria*) and tufted hair-grass (*Deschampsia cespitosa*) grow. Where it is dry, there are old hay meadow grasses – meadow foxtail (*Alopecurus pratensis*) and sweet vernal grass (*Anthoxanthum odoratum*). Other meadow species include: bugle (*Ajuga reptans*), common bird's-foot-trefoil (*Lotus corniculatus*) – growing on mounds, common sorrel (*Rumex acetosa*), germander speedwell (*Veronica chamaedrys*), meadow buttercup (*Ranunculus acris*), red clover (*Trifolium pratense*) and self-heal (*Prunella vulgaris*). These are common enough, but it was surprising to find wood anemone (*Anemone nemorosa*) with wide, dark green leaves growing in open sunlight in an old pasture.

The most distinctive feature of these pastures (in the eyes of the naturalist) we have saved for last. Abundant and widely distributed in both fields is a fern so small and so unfernlike as to be nearly invisible. This is adder's-tongue (*Ophioglossum vulgatum*), especially abundant at the lower end of the pastures, where the land incurves, perhaps where there is more moisture. Roots produce new plants by adventitious buds, accounting for the size of the populations.

Adder's-tongue has thrived, not only because of its reproductive potential, but also because Farmer Tustian does not turn the ground.

The Village Pond

Swerford village is exceptionally attractive. There are handsome period houses, but more than that, the village is off the main road; it has a sense of isolation. This quiet may be unappealing to some, to others it is a haven. One is 'in' the countryside; fields and woods, hills and valleys are a living panorama. East from Farmer Tustian's fields runs a road to the village green, and then, as it passes on, there is a village pond on the left, nearly hidden from view. We have seen that River Swere ponds, big and small, are man-made. This pond is man-made too, but it is high above the river and full of interesting life.

Would there were clean and well-tended village ponds in every village, where boys and girls of the local primary school could catch tadpoles, where wild and tame plants would be mixed together. Greater spearwort (*Ranunculus lingua*), for example, which grows in only one other site along the Swere – in the mill pond of Deddington Mill – grows in the Swerford village pond. It is rare in the county, more handsome and much larger than all other buttercups. Yellow iris (*Iris pseudacorus*) and bogbean (*Menyanthes trifoliata*), the only site of bogbean in the Swere river landscape, must have been planted too. The decorative pendulous sedge, *Carex pendula*, stands in the shallows, first among a genus of land plants that can colonize shallow water. It is an age in which the image on the screen has taken the place of seeing and touching in the out-of-doors. Think of the pond as a classroom laboratory, allowing an introduction to watery plant life and, more disturbing – but not usually for children – those fearful monsters, insects in their larval stages.

Wood anemone (*Anemone nemorosa*).

WOODLAND

WOODED SITES, both as spontaneous woodland where trees are self-sown, and plantations, which in one sense of the word are a group of planted trees and not exclusively, as one may see in Wales, a site of conifers in orderly rows, are a feature of the upper course of the River Swere. The Dingle is a tiny patch of wood above Barford St Michael; all the other mature Swere woods lie west of Wigginton, where the hills are steep and the valleys are narrow. In a sense, steep hills are an agent of woodland conservation, allowing trees to grow where they will, or inducing landowners to plant them. In all, there are seven sites of mature woodland along the Swere, and one along the northern tributaries. East of Swerford the river edge is intermittently wooded with what is in effect an overgrown hedge. Where the valley widens, the wooded edge becomes more interrupted, thinner and less concealing.

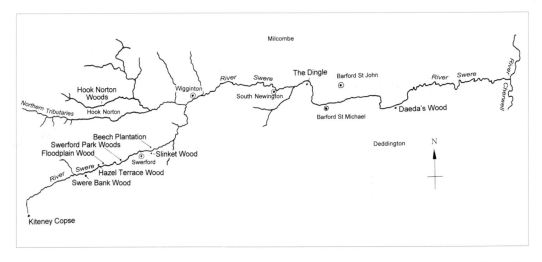

Of the eight woodland sites located on this map, The Dingle is a few mature trees and a scrubby hillside; all the rest are mature woods of the upper course of the River Swere and the northern tributaries. Villages on the river are marked with a dot within a circle.

Only Floodplain Wood is 'wet'; it is the wood with the greatest number of self-sown shrubs and trees and the greater variety of herbaceous flora. Even so, on its northern edge is a row of non-native black-Italian poplar (*Populus* 'Serotina') trees. The wooded sites of greatest extent have been planted. Swere Bank Wood, for example, is principally an ash (*Fraxinus excelsior*) plantation with herb-Paris (*Paris quadrifolia*) in rich loose soil, and guelder-rose (*Viburnum opulus*) and wayfaring-tree (*V. lantana*) on its edges. Swerford Park Woods have two parts: a mature beech (*Fagus sylvatica*) wood, so uniform in the age of the mature trees that we assume it to have been planted, and a belt of conifer trees, probably also planted. Of native trees in the Oxfordshire Uplands, ash is most often self-sown; sycamore (*Acer pseudoplatanus*), long naturalized, runs a close second. Ash occurs in every wood, even where beech is dominant, and nearly uniform in its cover of the ground. Beech, long prized for its elegance, forms a boulevard to the erstwhile entrance to Swerford Park, and is planted on the hillside wood below The Slinket; it is also planted above Island Marsh and Pond, where youthful beech trees are growing into a mature woodland plantation.

Paleo-botanists invite us to imagine a time when the British Isles were fully forested, trees mantling the earth like a spreading ocean. Surely there always were light gaps, sites where lightning felled giants, and later, places cleared where the first settlers made their encampments. The primeval forest, in another continent, is evoked by William Faulkner in his story *The Bear*: 'He ranged the summer woods, green with gloom ... where even at noon the sun fell only in windless dappling upon the earth which never completely died and which crawled with snakes ...' Of the young boy the author wrote: 'He stood for a moment – alone and lost in the green and soaring gloom of the markless wilderness.' In none of the Swere woods would one be lost, nor feel that green was gloom, or see snakes covering the ground, but in all there is the pleasure of mystery and dappled light.

Common to Rare Woody Plants

In all the woods, the tall trees are ash and sycamore; the small trees/shrubs are universally represented by blackthorn (*Prunus spinosa*), common hawthorn (*Crataegus monogyna*), elder (*Sambucus nigra*) and hazel (*Corylus avellana*); the woody climbers are blackberry (*Rubus fruticosus*) and ivy (*Hedera helix*). While these are the most common woody plants of the River Swere woods, others are only slightly less common: crack-willow (*Salix fragilis*) occurs at six sites, and grey willow (*S. cinerea*) and red currant (*Ribes rubrum*) at five; dogwood (*Cornus sanguineus*), European larch (*Larix decidua*), field maple (*Acer campestre* and honeysuckle (*Lonicera periclymenum*) occur at four sites. At the other extreme are woody plants that occur at only one site: goat willow (*Salix caprea*), gooseberry (*Ribes uva-crispa*), spindle (*Euonymus europaeus*), sweet chestnut (*Castanea sativa*) and yew (*Taxus baccata*).

Swerford Park: Two Plantations on One Estate

The woods of the park are divided from Floodplain Wood by a fence, an opening in the canopy, and a track. Whereas for the length of its passage along the side of Floodplain Wood the river worked its way without guidance, now it is managed for special effect. The Swere is shallow, chattering over stones, and about 3 m wide; it passes a small dam, after which it becomes deep and slow. The steep slopes of both the north and south sides of the river are densely wooded. Beech has nearly sole dominion of the south side where there is almost no shrub understorey. There is beech on the north side too, but on the lower levels of the adjoining hill the dominant trees are Norway spruce (*Picea abies*) and poplar (*Populus* sp.).

Beech and English oak

Beech and English oak (*Quercus robur*) trees have long won the hearts of the British people. Beech is tall and elegant, oak is muscular and strong. If we compare their distribution, we see that oak occurs at only one more site than beech:

Distribution of Beech and English Oak Trees Over Eight Sites

	1	2	3	4	5	6	7	8
Beech (*Fagus sylvatica*)	✓	✗	✓	✓	✓	✗	✓	✓
English Oak (*Quercus robur*)	✓	✓	✗	✓	✓	✓	✓	✓

Key: ✓ = present; ✗ = absent
Woodland sites are: (1) Kiteney Copse, (2) Swere Bank Wood, (3) Floodplain Wood, (4) Swerford Park Woods, (5) Slinket Wood, (6) The Dingle, (7) Hook Norton Woods, (8) beech plantation.

Of the six sites of beech, its presence in (1) and (3) is numerically insignificant, whereas in (4) and (8) it is dominant, and all other woody species in those sites are represented by only a few individuals, so difficult is it to flourish under a beech canopy.

The Slinket and Slinket Wood

The Slinket (an Anglo-Saxon word meaning narrow path) runs above both Little Bridge Marsh and Island Marsh and Pond; it is a grassy way giving a view to the top of the northern hills, used by Swerford residents for a stroll. The wood occupies the hillside below the path. At first, walking along The Slinket, there are several giant holly (*Ilex aquifolium*) trees and an irregular line of large hazel trees before coming to the hillside wood of now mature beech and oak trees, trees so tall and so wide-spreading that shade is continuous over the limits of the canopy.

Nevertheless, there are representative specimens of other species: common hawthorn, field maple, holly, sycamore and yew; grey willow maintains its possession of the riverside habitat. A spring on the lower slope of Slinket Wood has worn a hollow into its side, uncovering large boulders, and creating a moist and sheltered cove for the largest population of Hart's-tongue fern (*Phyllitis scolopendrium*) and the only site for soft shield-fern (*Polystichum setiferum*) along the river.

Top left: An avenue of beech (*Fagus sylvatica*) trees, once the entrance to Swerford Park.
Top right: Wayfaring-tree (*Viburnum lantana*), component of wooded edges of the river in its upper course.
Bottom left: Ramsons (*Allium ursinum*), a liliaceous plant abundant on the slopes of Hook Norton Woods and nowhere else.
Bottom right: Hook Norton Woods with mature sycamores (*Acer pseudoplatanus*) and a dense understorey of shrubs, including hazel (*Corylus avellana*).

Woodland Wildflowers

The shade of woodland tall trees helps to conserve moisture but has the disadvantage of limiting light to the woodland floor. One strategy of flowering plants beneath beech and oak is to rise early and flower before the tall trees have grown their leaves. As early as January, the leaf litter is whitened by snowdrops (*Galanthus nivalis*), the soil is pierced by bluebells (*Hyacinthoides non-scripta*) and by the young shoots of dog's mercury (*Mercurialis perennis*) and lords-and-ladies (*Arum maculatum*). Lesser celandine (*Ranunculus ficaria*) flowers early, at the same time as bluebell.

Bluebells and snowdrops, signs that winter is fleeing, flower before the canopy is closed. Other plants have a different strategy, many thriving in lower intensities of incoming sunlight. For them, the woodland floor, where light is scarce, is a habitat of reduced competition for space. Successful here are dog's mercury, hedge woundwort (*Stachys sylvatica*) and grasses such as false brome (*Brachypodium sylvaticum*), species common in Swere woods. As in any habitat, one may find a stray: in Slinket Wood it is ivy-leaved speedwell (*Veronica hederifolia*). There may be a rarity: an early-purple orchid (*Orchis mascula*) growing in a habitat suitable for its needs.

If we except the beech plantation above Island Marsh and Pond, the most common herbs, stalwarts of the woodland flora, are: cleavers (*Galium aparine*), common nettle (*Urtica dioica*), creeping buttercup (*Ranunculus repens*), dog's mercury, ground-ivy (*Glechoma hederacea*), hedge woundwort, herb-Robert (*Geranium robertianum*), lesser celandine, male-fern (*Dryopteris filix-mas*) and wood avens (*Geum urbanum*). Primrose (*Primula vulgaris*) occurs in only one of the eight woodland sites, and lady-fern (*Athyrium filix-femina*) is just as rare.

Top left: Swere Bank Wood, in winter light. Some of the cut logs, neatly stacked, have a rich covering of moss and lichens.

Bottom left: A view, looking north from the eastern end of The Slinket, of a wooden bridge over the Swere.

HOOK NORTON AND THE NORTHERN TRIBUTARY

UPRIVER, BEYOND THE VALLEY west of Wigginton, the River Swere has two branches. They are about equal in length, but the river that flows from Over Norton parish has the greater, and therefore the more reliable, flow of water. Perhaps it is evidence of this fact that only the Swere, flowing through Swerford, has two water-mill sites in its upper course, while the northern tributary, as we call the stream that arises above Hook Norton, has none. The beauty of the views down the steep banks along the stream, the sudden revelation of the largest marsh (Cradle Farm Marsh) along either branch, and finding chalk and acid meadows with some flowering plants unique to the northern tributary, lessens any other inequality between these branches.

The pond on Grounds Farm, in the parish of Hook Norton, with common bulrushes (*Typha latifolia*) and sedges (*Carex* sp.) around the edge and broad-leaved pondweed (*Potamogeton natans*) on the surface. Behind is the species-rich limestone meadow.

Hook Norton is an ancient town comfortable with the fame of its brewery, but in the sheep-grazed plateaux east from the pediments of the vanished railway line there is a landscape of a different beauty. Nowhere else did we find bitter-vetch (*Lathyrus linifolius*), heath speedwell (*Veronica officinalis*), heath spotted-orchid (*Dactylorhiza maculata* ssp. *ericetorum*), lousewort (*Pedicularis sylvatica*) and saw-wort (*Serratula tinctoria*), indicators of the more neutral to slightly acid soils occurring here. In the same way, gorse (*Ulex europaeus*), sheep's sorrel (*Rumex acetosella*) and tormentil (*Potentilla erecta*) are more widespread here than anywhere else in the valley. Whereas in the appearance of the meadows there are differences of aspect, and a sense of isolation in the lands of the northern tributary, limestone geology has created affinities with the site of the Swere Bank SSSI and with the meadow above The Meanders along the main stream.

Travelling east from Hook Norton, steep hillslopes slant down to the riverside. The sycamores (*Acer pseudoplatanus*), abundant on these slopes – they form a dense wood – have in many cases regenerated from stools; they are young trees and grow closely together, giving a very dark woodland shade. But when summer light plays through the leafage, the white-flowered ramsons (*Allium ursinum*) shine brightly. Ramsons, which are a botanical cousin of wild onions, occur only a short distance along the larger of the northern tributaries, where their density is spectacular. The steep banks of a shaded wood, with a north-facing aspect, are often a good place to look for ferns. This is a rich site, with broad buckler-fern (*Dryopteris dilatata*), hard shield-fern (*Polystichum aculeatum*), hart's-tongue (*Phyllitis scolopendrium*) and male-fern (*Dryopteris filix-mas*). Bluebells (*Hyacinthoides non-scripta*) and dog's mercury (*Mercurialis perennis*) occur in reasonable measure in the upper part of the wood, but not with the same abundance as ramsons. The marshy areas below the banks contain new species for the area such as lesser spearwort (*Ranunculus flammula*), pendulous sedge (*Carex pendula*) and southern marsh-orchid (*Dactylorhiza praetermissa*).

Below is a partial list of herbaceous species from the chalky and more acid banks of the northern tributary. Species with an asterisk occur only along the northern tributary; the other species are common to both streams above Wigginton, but occur infrequently and in isolated habitats.

Some Herbaceous Species from the Chalky and More Acid Banks of the Northern Tributary

Adder's-tongue (*Ophioglossum vulgatum*)	Heath Spotted-orchid (*Dactylorhiza maculata* ssp. *ericetorum*)*
Betony (*Stachys officinalis*)	
Bitter-vetch (*Lathyrus linifolius*)*	Lady's-mantle (*Alchemilla vulgaris*)
Common Centaury (*Centaurium erythraea*)	Lousewort (*Pedicularis sylvatica*)*
Common Milkwort (*Polygala vulgaris*)	Meadow Saxifrage (*Saxifraga granulata*)
Devil's-bit Scabious (*Succisa pratensis*)	Saw-wort (*Serratula tinctoria*)*
Dropwort (*Filipendula vulgaris*)	Sheep's Sorrel (*Rumex acetosella*)
Dwarf Thistle (*Cirsium acaule*)	Sneezewort (*Achillea ptarmica*)
Hairy Violet (*Viola hirta*)	Tormentil (*Potentilla erecta*)
Heath Speedwell (*Veronica officinalis*)*	Wood Club-rush (*Scirpus sylvaticus*)

Top left: Meadow saxifrage (*Saxifraga granulata*), like wood anemone, is a perennial herb. Notice that the flowering stems are glandular, the glands looking like dewdrops. **Top right:** Saw-wort (*Serratula tinctoria*), like thistles, is a member of the Asteraceae family. The bracts, which tightly enfold the flowers before they open, have a rich purple pattern and could be the edging of a clerical garment. **Bottom left:** Betony (*Stachys officinalis*) usually indicates a more acid soil and grows plentifully on the bank below Manor Farm. **Bottom right:** Lousewort (*Pedicularis sylvatica*).

Northern tributary of the River Swere beside Cradle Farm Marsh.

WIGGINTON MARSHES

THE WIGGINTON VALLEY begins at the westerly end of Paradise Farm, continues to the site of Wigginton's old corn-mill, and then, past the South Newington Road, it extends beyond The Meanders to the boundary of Milcombe parish. From the outset, the valley is wider than the narrow spaces beside the river in Swerford parish. Adjoining hills are less steep, have a more gradual slope and have relented from compressing the river basin. 'The red rich soil and the River Swere attracted Romano-British settlers. The site of a Roman Villa of some size and wealth, and possibly a military post, lies northeast of the church.'[28] For the first time, there is a footpath the length of, rather than only across, the valley, hugging the grassy slope on the north side of the river above The Meanders, east of the mill. All through the valley there is wet ground and moist grassland – in some wet places marsh plants are growing – but our focus is on two sites: Quarry Spring Marsh and Ribbon Marsh.

The Two Principal Marshes

Name of Site	Spring-fed	Dominants	Species Special to the Site
Quarry Spring Marsh	yes	*Juncus*	Common Spike-rush (*Eleocharis palustris*)
Ribbon Marsh	yes	none	Common Spike-rush (*Eleocharis palustris*)
			Skullcap (*Scutellaria galericulata*)
			Water-plantain (*Alisma plantago-aquatica*)

Quarry Spring Marsh

Quarry Spring Marsh lies between Wigginton village and Paradise Farm near, but not influenced by, the junction of the northern tributary with the Swere. The OS 191 map indicates the site of an old quarry – a circular concavity housing an active spring – the main source of the marsh below. Water runs downhill and lies quietly in the lowest level of the valley, west of the river; the marsh is probably fed by other springs, together supporting a shallow seasonal pond and very wet ground. At the quarry's spring, as well as in the runnel from it to the marsh below, are large stands of brooklime (*Veronica beccabunga*); fool's-water-cress (*Apium nodiflorum*) grows plentifully in the mouth of the old quarry, and ragged-Robin (*Lychnis flos-cuculi*) is present.

Quarry Spring Marsh has three zones. At the centre of the marsh is a small shallow pond; surrounding the pond, and beyond the margin of the soft dark muds, is common spike-rush (*Eleocharis palustris*), more abundant here than in any other site. Where the ground is wet and soft (even in the dry season) and criss-crossed by rills, hard rush (*Juncus inflexus*) and soft-rush (*J. effusus*) form tall tussocks, and dominate the greater space of the wetland.

Growing with *Juncus* is greater pond-sedge (*Carex riparia*); weakly represented, as associates, are common mouse-ear (*Cerastium fontanum*), floating sweet-grass (*Glyceria fluitans*), greater bird's-foot-trefoil (*Lotus pedunculatus*), jointed rush (*Juncus articulatus*), marsh thistle (*Cirsium palustre*) and smooth brome (*Bromus racemosus*). Beyond *Juncus*, slightly less wet ground is conspicuously dominated by tufted hair-grass (*Deschampsia cespitosa*), filling the outer envelope of the marsh.

In the wet meadow adjoining the marsh is more tufted hair-grass; also creeping bent (*Agrostis stolonifera*), crested dog's-tail (*Cynosurus cristatus*) and meadow foxtail (*Alopecurus pratensis*). Grey willow (*Salix cinerea*) continues to be more common than crack-willow (*S. fragilis*) along the river. The bank is crowded with great willowherb (*Epilobium hirsutum*) and hedge bindweed (*Calystegia sepium*), and the bank edge with branched bur-reed (*Sparganium erectum*).

Left: Wigginton in winter seen from The Meanders: the village name is Saxon for 'WICGA's place'; the mill was recorded in Domesday Book.

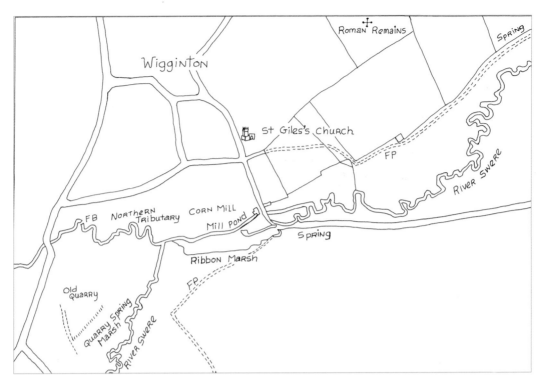

Map of Wigginton showing the sites of Quarry Spring Marsh and Ribbon Marsh.

Ribbon Marsh

Ribbon Marsh is a waving narrow band of vegetation, rooted in the shallow depression that is the course of the ancient river. Below the level of the Swere, west of the Wigginton bridge, the marsh occupies the valley floor, where the river would originally have flowed. The Swere was elevated long ago, held in a deep narrow channel – the upper leat – to amplify and control the power of the water for driving the corn-mill. The mill is gone, but the river continues to flow in the elevated channel.

The marsh marks the path of a sluggish stream. There is a lovely prospect from the bridge – tall sword-bladed yellow iris (*Iris pseudacorus*) punctuating the water's flow, tussocks of sedge with long elaborately pendent leaves, and the sweep uphill of an unimproved damp meadow rich with herbs and grasses on the south side of the marsh, with sheep and ponies at the western end. Depending on the season, water flows abundantly, or trickles, in the shallow mud-filled channel; one cannot see the water flow, so crowded is it with plant life, but its course can be traced by the ribbon of plants occupying it. Neither rush nor sedge is dominant. Instead, there are islets of vegetation between unoccupied spaces in the streambed.

Iris, sedge, meadowsweet, reed canary-grass and rush, or any combination of these, achieve local dominance, but none dominates the whole site. Each species forms a patch, mat or island of its own kind, no one species controlling the length of the gulley. Marsh horsetail (*Equisetum palustre*) is more numerous, plant for plant, than any other species without being dominant throughout the marsh. Almost unchanged since the Carboniferous Age, some 200 million years ago, the genus *Equisetum* has only 15 living species, 7 of which occur in the British Isles. All have greenish, ribbed, silica-laden stems.

Some species have their feet in the water, such as branched bur-reed and reed canary-grass (*Phalaris arundinacea*). Others prefer mushy ground – presumably their roots need not be so deep or penetrating – such as hemp-agrimony (*Eupatorium cannabinum*) and hard rush. Yet other species grow on the moist ground reaching toward the pasture – bristle club-rush (*Isolepis setacea*), creeping-Jenny (*Lysimachia nummularia*), cuckooflower (*Cardamine pratensis*) and marsh-marigold (*Caltha palustris*) – radiant in the height of flowering in mid-April, abundant in the marsh and growing in shallow, wet and muddy places.

Other plants conspicuous in the marsh are greater tussock-sedge (*Carex paniculata*), purple-loosestrife (*Lythrum salicaria*), water figwort (*Scrophularia auriculata*) and water-plantain (*Alisma plantago-aquatica*). Less conspicuous are common spike-rush, greater bird's-foot-trefoil, hoary willowherb (*Epilobium parviflorum*) and skullcap (*Scutellaria galericulata*). At the water's edge are brooklime, fool's-water-cress and water mint (*Mentha aquatica*).

Ragged-Robin (*Lychnis flos-cuculi*), with its deeply cleft rose-red petals, is one of the perennial beauties of Swere marshes and wet meadows. Each petal is cleft – these seem torn and hence ragged – more than once, 3–4 clefts per petal. Ragged-Robin is a member of the same family, the Caryophyllaceae, as are the red and white campions and the Deptford pink.

The meadow of the south slope is interesting for the richness of its populations of herbs, not throughout the large space but in specific areas of the greatest moisture. The upper slope is drier, and grass dominates. An irregularly wide band of silverweed (*Potentilla anserina*) marks the point of transition to the higher and drier grassland with meadow buttercup (*Ranunculus acris*) and creeping thistle (*Cirsium arvense*). Here is a list of the highlights of the meadow above Ribbon Marsh; Quarry Spring Meadow has similar species: betony (*Stachys officinalis*), cat's-ear (*Hypochaeris radicata*), common bird's-foot-trefoil (*Lotus corniculatus*), common spotted-orchid (*Dactylorhiza fuchsii*), devil's-bit scabious (*Succisa pratensis*), dropwort (*Filipendula vulgaris*), field wood-rush (*Luzula campestris*), hairy sedge (*Carex hirta*), lady's-bedstraw (*Galium verum*), lady's-mantle (*Alchemilla vulgaris*), meadow saxifrage (*Saxifraga granulata*), pignut (*Conopodium majus*), red bartsia (*Odontites verna*), salad burnet (*Sanguisorba minor* ssp. *minor*) and tormentil (*Potentilla erecta*).

Top left: Looking west along the course of Ribbon Marsh. Recently, heavy rains of early autumn have filled the channel, covering the grasses of summer that now look like marine algae; notice the effect of summer grazing on the tall marsh plants.

Top right: Marsh horsetail (*Equisetum palustre*). The picture shows clearly both the green grooved and branched stems rising higher than the more conspicuous spore-bearing bodies on their own stems.

Bottom: Summer in Ribbon Marsh. The tall, dark green blades of yellow iris (*Iris pseudacorus*) are the most prominent feature of a wetland in which the flowers of spring become the fruits of summer.

INTRODUCING GRASSLANDS

'M EADOW' is a hay-scented word, evocative of the cuckoo and cowslip, of the haywain and harvest in Constable's time. A field is less lush; it may be on higher ground, above the flood meadows. River Swere fields are dark green or yellow, set to corn or oilseed rape. If a field is grazed, or left idle, dock and nettle settle in; if it is sown to corn, arable weeds, like common fumitory and shepherd's purse, long attached to man's agricultural civilizations, will grow there too.

A field is never as colourful, or as enchanting, as an old hay meadow in flower. Old hay meadows in Swere parishes are limestone grasslands, mainly along the middle course of the river, where the river valley is underlain by Chipping Norton Limestone. Pretty as they are, old hay meadows are not a natural habitat of the British Isles. Hills and valleys of the prehistoric past were covered in woodland, except where there was marsh, river or scree. 'All sites of old grassland, almost without exception, were once wildwood and revert to woodland in a few decades if not grazed or mown.'[29]

Limestone grassland of The Meanders, the shrubs defining the line of the river.

Top left: Yorkshire-fog (*Holcus lanatus*), the most common grass, occurring at 100% of the 14 grassland sites. **Top right:** Meadow barley (*Hordeum secalinum*), an indicator of undisturbed grasslands, and a rare plant along the Swere. **Bottom left:** Crested dog's-tail (*Cynosurus cristatus*), occurring at 93% of the grassland sites. **Bottom right:** Cock's-foot (*Dactylis glomerata*), occurring at 93% of Swere meadows.

Top: Oxeye daisy (*Leucanthemum vulgare*), which occurs at 5 of the 14 grassland sites, here with red clover (*Trifolium pratense*), the fruiting stalks of common sorrel (*Rumex acetosa*) and, in the foreground, yellow-rattle (*Rhinanthus minor*) – a rich floral composition, characteristic of what is best in old hay meadows.
Bottom: Swere grassland with meadow crane's-bill (*Geranium pratense*) prominent in a field of wildflowers.

In the floodplain meadows along the River Cherwell, the sheep-stocking rate is high and plant diversity low. Deddington parish fields are magnificent in the quality, size and uniformity of crops grown, but there are no old hay meadows there. In the middle course of the Swere, there are two small and three medium grassland meadows that have a flora richer than any other in the area. The small meadows are on the south side of the river in Swerford parish, below the motte and bailey of Norman occupation in Swerford village. The farmer of one of the small pastures for a handful of cows, told us he has never turned the ground. The other small meadow is an ungrazed slope above Little Bridge Marsh.

Of larger grasslands, the richest is the Swere Bank SSSI in Hook Norton parish overlying the Great Oolite Limestone, with at least 67 species of herbaceous plants including 12 that occur at only that site. Another limestone grassland is in the Milcombe valley; a third is the meadow (and marsh) above The Meanders. Grassy banks beside the northern tributary of the Swere, in Hook Norton parish, are speckled with stands of betony (*Stachys officinalis*) and other lovers of more neutral soils. A table of the species composition of all the meadows is in Appendix II.

Looking down the steep slope from the motte and bailey in the village of Swerford to the small cluster of houses where the river crosses Between Towns Road, with a view of the Hereford x Friesian cattle on their unimproved native grassland.

MARSH AND MEADOW OF THE MEANDERS

THE RICHNESS of the riverside meadow, annually flooded and overlain with silts and organic debris, was probably the most valuable asset of a low-lying farm before the advent of the chemical industry. In many Oxfordshire valleys in the Roman period, alluvial meadows were managed on a large scale; it was then that evidence for the mowing of hay-meadows occurs for the first time.[30] There are sixteen Swere meadows – twelve on the Swere proper, four on its northern tributary. From Swerford to Deddington there are 131 species of flowering plants in the meadows. One of the richest of these is in Wigginton parish. 'Meander' is from Maiandros, a winding river on the Anatolian plateau, once the kingdom of Phrygia. In places, the Swere is straight, it follows the will of man, who made it into a canal; otherwise the river's way is wilful and vagrant. In the valley of The Meanders, for example, where there are no trees to conceal the river's movement, splendid S-shaped figures have been carved out of the alluvium – a textbook figuration of 'valley and channel landscape morphology'.

Looking toward the village of Wigginton, once the domain of a Saxon lord, the extreme sinuosity of the River Swere in the broad alluvial valley is clearly visible. Like tall whiskbrooms, two pollard crack-willows mark the river's edge. The village buildings nearest the river are on the site of the old mill.

Top left: This photograph shows how abundantly yellow-rattle (*Rhinanthus minor*) grows in the meadow of The Meanders. **Top right:** A close look at the yellow-rattle flowers, and the linear leaves which alternate in pairs and have points on the margins. **Bottom left:** Goat's-beard (*Tragopogon pratensis*), showing the hemispheric geometry of its fruiting head, with the fine hairs of each seed-end touching its neighbour's like a spider's web. **Bottom right:** A close-up of dropwort (*Filipendula vulgaris*), a species found in only a few sites in the landscapes of Swere valley meadows, always where there is calcareous ground.

In addition to the deposition of silts and sediments, there is an extra benefit to winter-meadow flooding. The covering of water acts as a blanket, keeping the soil warmer than hillside soils; when the water drains away in early spring, the meadow has the early grass. East of Wigginton, marsh and meadow lie together above the meandering river. Fed by a spring on a soil-mantled hillside above the marsh and meadow, the marsh is sustained by a catchment of water, just seen in the centre of the photograph on page 92. In June, there were thousands of yellow-rattle plants (*Rhinanthus minor*); at the same time pignut (*Conopodium majus*) was in flower and Chimney Sweeper moths (*Odezia atrata*) were abundant. In general, rich grasslands of Swere valleys lie on sloping ground overlying limestone; in all these, except the SSSI, springs create pockets of wetness and a greater richness of wildflower species.

Some of the butterflies seen over the meadow:
Top left: Small Tortoiseshell (*Aglais urticae*). **Top right:** Common Blue (*Polyommatus icarus*). **Bottom left:** Small Copper (*Lycaena phlaeas*). **Bottom right:** Painted Lady (*Vanessa cardui*). Both the Small Tortoiseshell and the Painted Lady are shown alighted on hemp-agrimony (*Eupatorium cannabinum*), a plant of Swere marshes and known to be attractive to many butterflies.

Top: The River Swere, so still and shallow in the height of summer, as it leaves The Meanders; meadowsweet (*Filipendula ulmaria*) bunches by the edge on the right side and reed canary-grass (*Phalaris arundinacea*) on the left. **Bottom:** Common bird's-foot-trefoil (*Lotus corniculatus*), a regular inhabitant of the rich meadows along the Swere, occurring at 12 out of 14 sites.

First and foremost, a meadow (*maed*, literally 'mowed') is a habitat of grasses. Grasses bind the soil, hold it deeply, and resist the onset of blackthorn (*Prunus spinosa*) and other scouts of the succession to woodland. If one is susceptible to the irritation of grass pollens, the aesthetic experience is somewhat lessened by itchy eyes. In the meadow of The Meanders, there are 14 grass species. Not all are distinctive of base-rich soils and undisturbed ground. Cock's-foot (*Dactylis glomerata*) and false oat-grass (*Arrhenatherum elatius*), for example, are nearly universal on the verges; Yorkshire-fog (*Holcus lanatus*) is hardy, thriving in rough ground, weedy in its toughness. Perennial rye-grass (*Lolium perenne*) is a native fodder grass able to reseed itself on field margins, and not distinctive of calcareous grassland. Creeping bent (*Agrostis stolonifera*), meadow fescue (*Festuca pratensis*), meadow foxtail (*Alopecurus pratensis*) and smooth meadow-grass (*Poa pratensis*) are here, but they are common and occur in most of the meadows along the Swere. Quaking-grass (*Briza media*), tor-grass (*Brachypodium pinnatum*) and upright brome (*Bromopsis erecta*) are absent as they only occur on our limestone grassland sites, but the uncommon meadow barley (*Hordeum secalinum*) with crested dog's-tail (*Cynosurus cristatus*), sweet vernal-grass (*Anthoxanthum odoratum*) and yellow oat-grass (*Trisetum flavescens*) are present and are good indicators of ancient pastures.

Red clover (*Trifolium pratense*).

In both pictures, the river is making its exit from the Wigginton valley, and has given up the exhibition of meandering, which it performed so well there. Notice the riffling of the stream, in the left photograph, and then, before the bridge of its final exit, in the photograph below, and before passing on to the area of Peat Marsh, the river deepens. The red berries on the small tree past the bridge belong to common hawthorn (*Crataegus monogyna*), a plant that adds colour to the landscape in every season.

Herbs of Marsh and Meadow

The water-table varies over the slope of the hill, creating conditions conducive to the intermingling of marsh and meadow species, as much as to their segregation. Cuckooflower (*Cardamine pratensis*), for example, is as comfortable in the wet meadow as on the edge of the wetter marsh; field wood-rush (*Luzula campestris*) usually grows farther away from wet ground than marsh horsetail (*Equisetum palustre*), but here it grows both in the meadow and the marsh. Meadow saxifrage (*Saxifraga granulata)* and salad burnet (*Sanguisorba minor* ssp. *minor*), both indicators of limestone grassland, grow above the marsh spring. Yellow-rattle grows in the meadow but also in the spaces occupied by lesser pond-sedge (*Carex acutiformis*) and yellow iris (*Iris pseudacorus*).

The Herbs of the Marsh and Meadow of The Meanders

Bulbous Buttercup (*Ranunculus bulbosus*)	Lesser Pond-sedge (*Carex acutiformis*)
Burnet-saxifrage (*Pimpinella saxifraga*)	Marsh Horsetail (*Equisetum palustre*)
Carnation Sedge (*Carex panicea*)	Marsh-marigold (*Caltha palustris*)
Common Bird's-foot-trefoil (*Lotus corniculatus*)	Marsh Thistle (*Cirsium palustre*)
Common Knapweed (*Centaurea nigra*)	Meadow Buttercup (*Ranunculus acris*)
Common Marsh-bedstraw (*Galium palustre*)	Meadow Crane's-bill (*Geranium pratense*)
Common Mouse-ear (*Cerastium fontanum*)	Meadow Saxifrage (*Saxifraga granulata*)
Common Sorrel (*Rumex acetosa*)	Meadowsweet (*Filipendula ulmaria*)
Cow Parsley (*Anthriscus sylvestris*)	Meadow Vetchling (*Lathyrus pratensis*)
Cowslip (*Primula veris*)	Oxeye Daisy (*Leucanthemum vulgare*)
Creeping Buttercup (*Ranunculus repens*)	Pignut (*Conopodium majus*)
Cuckooflower (*Cardamine pratensis*)	Ragged-Robin (*Lychnis flos-cuculi*)
Dropwort (*Filipendula vulgaris*)	Red Clover (*Trifolium pratense*)
Field Wood-rush (*Luzula campestris*)	Ribwort Plantain (*Plantago lanceolata*)
Germander Speedwell (*Veronica chamaedrys*)	Salad Burnet (*Sanguisorba minor* ssp. *minor*)
Goat's-beard (*Tragopogon pratensis*)	Selfheal (*Prunella vulgaris*)
Greater Knapweed (*Centaurea scabiosa*)	Silverweed (*Potentilla anserina*)
Hairy Sedge (*Carex hirta*)	White Clover (*Trifolium repens*)
Hemp-agrimony (*Eupatorium cannabinum*)	Yellow Iris (*Iris pseudacorus*)
Lady's Bedstraw (*Galium verum*)	Yellow-rattle (*Rhinanthus minor*)
Lesser Celandine (*Ranunculus ficaria*)	

Top right: Dropwort (*Filipendula vulgaris*) standing tall in the foreground and, in the distance, the width of the meadow is framed by meadow buttercup (*Ranunculus acris*).
Middle right: The white mist in the centre of the photograph is common marsh-bedstraw (*Galium palustre*), with meadow buttercup.
Bottom right: Meadow crane's-bill (*Geranium pratense*), with palmately-lobed leaves and violet-blue flowers, grows among cow parsley (*Anthriscus sylvestris*), with white flat-topped umbels.

Soil Chemistry and Plant Life

ONE VIEW of life is that it is 'all chemistry'. Because cell dynamics are intelligible in terms of chemical reactions, this view has a wide currency, but the field botanist rarely thinks of plant populations solely in terms of chemistry. On the other hand, plant species may be clear indicators of soil chemical conditions. In addition to carbon, hydrogen and oxygen, which can be absorbed from water or from the atmosphere, plants require a number of minerals which must be taken in from the soil. Seven elements that the plant requires in large amounts are nitrogen, potassium, calcium, phosphorus, sulphur, iron and magnesium.

Since many plants grow best under specific conditions of soil chemistry, their very presence is an indicator of those conditions. A large population of *Rhododendron* in a wild wood, for example, would be a strong indication of acid soil. Some of these conditions have been codified in Ellenburg's indicator values for British plants,[31] otherwise known as E-numbers.

Every flowering plant in the Swere river landscapes may be assigned an E-number, but what is especially interesting are the E-number values of plants we think of as belonging to undisturbed grasslands. Below is a selection of five species that are special to the grasslands between the SSSI and South Newington.

If a grassland is undisturbed, it means the ground is not turned and therefore enriched with nitrogen. In the E-number table, N = nitrogen and a low number (on a scale of 1–9) indicates infertile soil. For example, 1 indicates extremely infertile sites; 2–3 indicates more or less infertile sites. In the list of five species, N-values range 2–3. These are plants that 'like' infertile soils!

In the River Swere fields and meadows, the geology fully confirms this usage, as do the N-numbers. What about R-values, soil pH? A 1 indicates extreme acidity; 3 is an acid indicator; 5 is an indicator of moderately acid soils; 6-7 indicates soils that are weakly acid to

A Selection of Species Belonging to Undisturbed Grasslands, with their E-numbers

	R	N	Sites
Burnet-saxifrage (*Pimpinella saxifraga*)	7	3	7
Common Rock-rose (*Helianthemum nummularium*)	7	2	1
Devil's-bit Scabious (*Succisa pratensis*)	5	2	5
Lady's Bedstraw (*Galium verum*)	6	2	11
Salad Burnet (*Sanguisorba minor* ssp. *minor*)	8	3	10

Key: R = alkalinity/acidity, N = nitrogen, Sites = number of sites in Swere landscapes

weakly basic; 8 is rising higher toward the basic end of the scale. But the numbers alone cannot explain the frequency of the plant's distribution. Otherwise *Helianthemum* would occur more frequently, and be seen at least as often as *Pimpinella*. That is because plant life is not just all chemistry.

A splendid view of the leaf litter in Hook Norton Woods, east of Hook Norton village, along a northern tributary of the River Swere. Nutrients are recycled through plant and animal bodies – earthworms and pillbugs, for example – and returned to the soil, broken down and taken up into the plants again. For this reason, some naturalists speak of the 'living soil'.

HORSE-PASTURE POND AND MARSH

HERE TOO, as at Long Marsh and Pond, water arises from springs on the calcareous grasslands and percolates downhill, forming a marsh in the cusp of the valley and a pond which has been enlarged to assuage a horse's thirst. Long blades of branched bur-reed (*Sparganium erectum*) dominate the Horse-Pasture Pond in summer, a plant that roots in mud or shallow water, and even more abundantly in slowly moving stretches of the river.

Pond and marsh account for 22 species of herbaceous plants including cuckooflower (*Cardamine pratensis*), fool's-water-cress (*Apium nodiflorum*), hemp-agrimony (*Eupatorium cannabinum*), marsh-marigold (*Caltha palustris*), ragged-Robin (*Lychnis flos-cuculi*), water-plantain (*Alisma plantago-aquatica*) and winter-cress (*Barbarea vulgaris*). A dragonfly, the Broad-bodied Chaser, hovered over the shallow pond, and nearby a Common Blue Damselfly perched momentarily on a *Sparganium* blade. Ponds are not always beautiful, but their life is exotic, and it arouses in us a special pleasure, one which children may feel keenly. Water dock (*Rumex hydrolapathum*) grows on the river edge, a short walk from the pond, but not anywhere else along the Swere.

Horse-Pasture Pond and Marsh in late summer.

Disturbed ground, such as the heavily manured surrounds of a pond, is an ideal habitat for celery-leaved buttercup (*Ranunculus sceleratus*), a species found at the edge of Horse-Pasture Pond. The plant community of this pond edge, which shelves gradually into the water, is tolerant of inundation alternating with desiccation, as well as of nitrogen-rich soils.[32] Celery-leaved buttercup is particularly indicative of such soils (Ellenburg N value of 8) and does not occur again on the Swere until it nears the junction with the River Cherwell.

Hemp-agrimony (*Eupatorium cannabinum*).

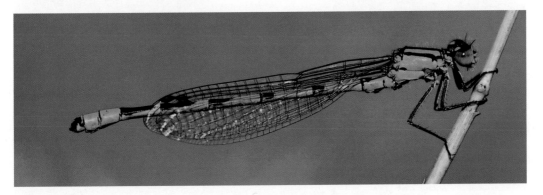

Common Blue Damselfly (*Enallagma cyathigerum*), often seen over ponds along the Swere. Typically of damselflies, the wings are folded back and held against the long body when at rest; notice how short the antennae are, compared to ants, bees and butterflies.

Top: Horse-Pasture Pond and Marsh in early summer, with branched bur-reed (*Sparganium erectum*) growing in the pond. **Bottom:** The pond in the winter.

The top photograph opposite shows the pond and marsh in early summer dress, with wild angelica (*Angelica sylvestris*), hemp-agrimony and water figwort (*Scrophularia auriculata*) being visible round the edge of the pond. White water-lilies (*Nymphaea alba*) decorate the surface. The bottom photograph shows that winter has whitened the landscape and darkened the pond, increasing the reflective capacity of its surface. Beneath the water is a large population of Canadian waterweed (*Elodea canadensis*), naturalized in canals and rivers throughout Great Britain. At the eastern end of the same meadow is another small spring-fed pond, Pony Pond, with water-crowfoot species – pond water-crowfoot (*Ranunculus peltatus*) and thread-leaved water-crowfoot (*R. trichophyllus*) – and spiked water-milfoil (*Myriophyllum spicatum*).

Very near the pond, the river meanders slowly. On muddy shores, fool's-water-cress (*Apium nodiflorum*) grows abundantly. At the edge of the stream can be seen blue water-speedwell (*Veronica anagallis-aquatica*) and the seeding spikes of winter-cress.

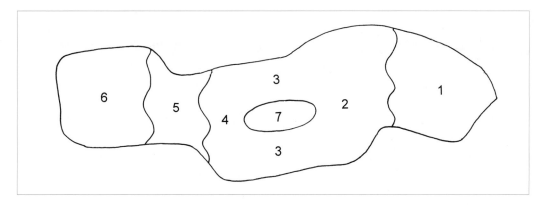

Diagram of the seven zones of vegetation in Long Marsh, Milcombe valley; the herbaceous species are listed in the table on pages 110–111.

A variety of species of *Juncus* – blunt-flowered rush (*J. subnodulosus*), hard rush (*J. inflexus*), sharp-flowered rush (*J. acutiflorus*), soft-rush (*J. effusus*) – composes individual stands, some large, outside the area of *Carex acuta*'s dominance. At the eastern end of the pond is a nearly pure stand of reed canary-grass (*Phalaris arundinacea*); and Zone 4 is the only site of brown sedge (*Carex disticha*) along the Swere. In the list of herbaceous species, dominant (d), subdominant (sd), and associated (a) species are identified for each zone, including the species of the outer edge of the marsh, being the outer limit of Zone 3. At that edge it is less wet than in the inner spaces; it is there, on the 'crust of the baguette', that marsh horsetail (*Equisetum palustre*) is abundant. This is the zone of the greatest flowering plant diversity, with 24 species represented.

Top left: A swathe of marsh in a valued grassland, the hay taken from the land to the marsh edge. The height of the sudden drop into the mushy ground of the marsh, from its edge, is not visible.
Middle left: A handsome patch of yellow iris (*Iris pseudacorus*).
Bottom left: Slender tufted-sedge (*Carex acuta*), with its bright green and curved blades, and a dotting of iris. The marsh is a mosaic of habitats, each varying in some degree of wetness, and also of access to light. Some species, such as the cuckooflower (*Cardamine pratensis*) and marsh-marigold (*Caltha palustris*), flower early thus avoiding the light-blocking effect of the taller sedges which grow more slowly in spring.

Right: Yellow iris (*Iris pseudacorus*).

Herbaceous Species of Long Marsh and Pond

ZONES	1	2	3	4	5	6	7
Amphibious Bistort (*Persicaria amphibia*)	✗	✗	✗	✗	✗	✗	a
Blunt-flowered Rush (*Juncus subnodulosus*)	✗	✗	✗	✗	✗	✗	a
Branched Bur-reed (*Sparganium erectum*)	✗	d	a	✗	d	✗	✗
Broad-leaved Pondweed (*Potamogeton natans*)	✗	✗	a	✗	✗	✗	✗
Brown Sedge (*Carex disticha*)	✗	✗	✗	a	✗	✗	✗
Common Duckweed (*Lemna minor*)	✗	✗	sd	✗	✗	✗	✗
Common Marsh-bedstraw (*Galium palustre*)	✗	✗	✗	✗	a	✗	a
Common Sorrel (*Rumex acetosa*)	✗	✗	✗	✗	a	✗	a
Common Spike-rush (*Eleocharis palustris*)	✗	✗	✗	✗	✗	✗	a
Compact Rush (*Juncus conglomeratus*)	✗	✗	sd	✗	✗	✗	✗
Creeping Buttercup (*Ranunculus repens*)	✗	✗	✗	✗	✗	✗	a
Cuckooflower (*Cardamine pratensis*)	✗	✗	✗	✗	✗	✗	a
False Oat-grass (*Arrhenatherum elatius*)	✗	✗	✗	✗	✗	✗	a
Floating Sweet-grass (*Glyceria fluitans*)	✗	a	✗	✗	✗	✗	a
Greater Bird's-foot-trefoil (*Lotus pedunculatus*)	✗	a	✗	✗	a	✗	a
Greater Pond-sedge (*Carex riparia*)	a	✗	✗	a	✗	a	✗
Hairy Sedge (*Carex hirta*)	✗	✗	✗	✗	✗	✗	a
Hard Rush (*Juncus inflexus*)	✗	a	✗	✗	✗	✗	✗
Lesser Celandine (*Ranunculus ficaria*)	✗	✗	✗	✗	✗	✗	a
Lesser Pond-sedge (*Carex acutiformis*)	✗	✗	a	✗	a	✗	✗
Lesser Stitchwort (*Stellaria graminea*)	✗	✗	✗	✗	✗	✗	a
Marsh Horsetail (*Equisetum palustre*)	✗	✗	✗	✗	a	✗	d
Marsh-marigold (*Caltha palustris*)	✗	✗	a	✗	✗	✗	✗
Marsh Thistle (*Cirsium palustre*)	✗	✗	✗	✗	✗	✗	a
Meadow Crane's-bill (*Geranium pratense*)	a	✗	✗	✗	✗	✗	a
Meadow Foxtail (*Alopecurus pratensis*)	✗	✗	✗	✗	✗	✗	a
Meadowsweet (*Filipendula ulmaria*)	d	✗	✗	✗	✗	d	✗
Meadow Vetchling (*Lathyrus pratensis*)	✗	✗	✗	✗	✗	✗	a
Purple-loosestrife (*Lythrum salicaria*)	✗	a	✗	✗	a	✗	✗
Ragged-Robin (*Lychnis flos-cuculi*)	✗	✗	✗	✗	✗	✗	a
Reed Canary-grass (*Phalaris arundinacea*)	d	a	✗	✗	✗	✗	✗
Sharp-flowered Rush (*Juncus acutiflorus*)	✗	a	✗	✗	✗	✗	✗
Silverweed (*Potentilla anserina*)	✗	✗	✗	✗	✗	✗	a
Skullcap (*Scutellaria galericulata*)	✗	✗	✗	✗	✗	✗	a
Slender Tufted-sedge (*Carex acuta*)	✗	a	a	d	✗	d	✗
Smooth Meadow-grass (*Poa pratensis*)	✗	✗	✗	✗	✗	✗	a
Soft-rush (*Juncus effusus*)	✗	a	a	a	✗	✗	✗
Square-stalked St John's-wort (*Hypericum tetrapterum*)	✗	✗	✗	✗	✗	✗	a

Tufted Hair-grass (*Deschampsia cespitosa*)	✗	✗	✗	✗	✗	✗	a
Water Figwort (*Scrophularia auriculata*)	a	✗	✗	✗	✗	✗	✗
Water Mint (*Mentha aquatica*)	✗	a	✗	✗	✗	✗	✗
Water-plantain (*Alisma plantago-aquatica*)	✗	✗	✗	✗	a	✗	✗
Winter-cress (*Barbarea vulgaris*)	✗	✗	a	✗	✗	✗	✗
Wood Club-rush (*Scirpus sylvaticus*)	✗	a	✗	✗	✗	✗	✗
Yellow Iris (*Iris pseudacorus*)	✗	✗	✗	✗	d	✗	✗
Yellow Water-lily (*Nuphar lutea*)	✗	✗	d	✗	✗	✗	✗
Yorkshire-fog (*Holcus lanatus*)	✗	✗	✗	✗	✗	✗	a
TOTAL SPECIES/ZONE	**5**	**11**	**10**	**4**	**9**	**3**	**25**

Key: ✗ = not in this zone; a = associated; d = dominant; sd = subdominant

Long Marsh and Pond in the summer, showing the abundance of greater pond-sedge (*Carex riparia*) and the density of plant life in the pond.

BUTTERBUR

SEEING BUTTERBUR (*Petasites hybridus*), one doesn't say, Ah, what a lovely flower! It seems out of place. The leaves are large (10-90 cm across), and the plants grow closely together, forming dense colonies; the greatest of these are along the Swere covering the entire area of a low alluvial plain on land of the former South Newington mill. Locally it is called 'jungle rhubarb'. Abundant along the river in the middle course, butterbur is a perennial with a tuberous-thickened base. It occurs at seven sites between South Newington and Wigginton, once in each of the Barfords, at Deddington Mill and twice along the northern tributary, more often in semi-shade than open sunshine. It is interesting that butterbur does not occur on the main river west of Wigginton; it first occurs on the northern tributary east of Hook Norton. Butterbur thrives on nutrient-rich soils (Ellenburg N value 7). The sexes have a curious relationship. Not only do male and female flowers occur on separate plants, which of course is not an uncommon arrangement among plants, but, more unusually, females are far less plentiful than males. Female plants have been reported from only one location in Oxfordshire, one out of a possible 596 tetrads; males have been reported from 108. Both sexes occur in the large colony near the South Newington mill and along the northern tributary. Butterbur performs a useful function in riverine ecology: it collects and holds soil on the floodplain, building a terrace where shrubs and trees will root and flourish.

Butterbur (*Petasites hybridus*). Plant names, like the names of fields, conserve the memory of uses no longer practiced. 'Dairy Grounds', for example, is a common name of a farm field where dairy cows no longer graze, just as butter is no longer neatly wrapped in the elephantine leaves of this member of the daisy family.

Left: The male flower. **Right:** The female flower. **Bottom:** Butterbur in semi-open moist woodland. This particularly large stand is found between the upper leat of the South Newington mill and the River Swere.

THE BAULK

THE BAULK is a short track with high banks on a steep incline descending from the A361, without any hint from above that there is a ford over the River Swere at the bottom, and just east of South Newington. By definition, a baulk is 'a strip of ground left unploughed as a boundary line between two ploughed portions.'[34] The western edge of The Baulk, as Julian Barbour has written in the newsletter of South Newington's Dyson Society, formed the boundary between the parishes of Milcombe and South Newington.[35] There is good reason, he writes, to assume that the parish boundary had remained unchanged (before the 1980s) for centuries if not more than a millennium. The Baulk is an eroded track, sculpted out of the soft underlying bedrock. Some villagers say that the eroded track is the route of the old coaching road; this accounts for its depth, worn down by many a carriage. But others say, with equal conviction, that it was worn down before the coaching era by traffic from Milcombe village to its mill near the river. The question of the origin of The Baulk adds interest and sparkle to meetings of the village history society; but let me return to questions of plant life. The presence of common knapweed (*Centaurea nigra*) and salad burnet (*Sanguisorba minor* ssp. *minor*), on the banks of The Baulk, indicates a limestone substrate.

The ford at South Newington.

Hop (*Humulus lupulus*), one of the wild species found growing in The Baulk. Hop is a perennial herbaceous climber, its stems twisting in a clockwise direction, and its flowers and fruits – the fruits that are used in brewing – hang gracefully from the climbing stem. Hop has been seen in several places along the Swere, but mostly along the upper course in high hedges in Swerford parish.

This same substrate is probably continuous with the rock underlying the grasslands from above Wigginton and through the Milcombe valley. Like the cliffs of Dover, and depending on the direction of one's travel, The Baulk is the last upsurge or the herald of a limestone geology.

Much more enchanting than the track itself is its destination: no other site, anywhere along the Swere, is of such immediate attraction to villagers of every age as the ford at South Newington. Would that every village could have such a meeting place, where the water is wilful and the fields are tame. A little bridge, shown in the photograph opposite, and a bench nearby, invite a quiet moment. And for the young of South Newington, summer invites the adventure of wading in the river where there is no danger of being swept away.

The Baulk attracts the goodwill of villagers with plantings, trees and flowers such as *Narcissus*. Among the 16 herbaceous species wild in The Baulk, these are noteworthy: agrimony (*Agrimonia eupatoria*), common knapweed, common toadflax (*Linaria vulgaris*), creeping cinquefoil (*Potentilla reptans*), greater knapweed (*Centaurea scabiosa*), hop (*Humulus lupulus*), salad burnet and wild basil (*Clinopodium vulgare*).

ALDER TREES

ALDER TREES are more distinctive, standing in a series along the river edge, and more ceremonial in this role than any other tree along the Swere. They are the principal tree of the middle course of the river, and generally absent from the upper and lower courses. Why is this? So far, no explanation has been given. But we do know that in 1794 the river east of the South Newington ford was straightened. The photograph below shows the alder (*Alnus glutinosa*) to its best advantage in this stretch of the river, dotting the bank at regular intervals for a short distance – and then again out of the picture's frame.

Birch, hazel and hornbeam belong to the same family as alder (Betulaceae); like alder, they have catkins. Male catkins give the tree its rufous-purple tint in March when winter looks for a herald of spring. Ever since the appearance of alder in the wildwood of post-glacial Britain – about 8000 BP ('before the present') – this tree has inhabited wet places in woods and by lakes and streams, in association with oak, pine and hazel. With its dense mass of rootlets, no other tree is so well-adapted for holding together the banks of rivers and ought, for utility as well as for beauty, to be more often planted along the Swere.

Alder (*Alnus glutinosa*) trees along the straightened River Swere east of South Newington.

Top left: Alder trees in March. **Top right:** Bright sunlight amplifies the naturally luminous quality of the leaves, green and glabrous on both sides. **Bottom:** The same trees as in the photograph opposite on the left, but in rare winter dress.

WATER-MILLS ON THE RIVER SWERE

WHEN THE WATER-MILL appeared in the late Roman Empire, a new dimension was added to the history of society and technology – an alternative to ox and slave. The invention spread rapidly; troops of the Roman garrison on Hadrian's Wall were using water-driven corn-mills at three places, but we know nothing more of water-mills in the British Isles until AD 762. 'The earliest reliable allusion to a corn-mill in England occurs in a charter granted by Ethelbert of Kent in 762 to the owners of a monastic mill near Dover.'[36] In its detailed panorama, Domesday Book (1087) gives the best picture of the state of England at the end of the Anglo-Saxon period when there were 5,624 water-mills, 200 of which were in Oxfordshire. As for the Swere, Richard Davis of Lewknor's map of the county shows nine mills in 1794, many of which, we presume, had been in existence for centuries.

The mill house at South Newington.

We have no record of how Swere mill wheels operated, but we know from Philip Page, of South Newington, that both the mill of that village and the Milcombe Mill nearby, which in their last days belonged to his family, were driven by undershot wheels. Undershot wheels worked best in 'swiftly flowing rivers with fairly constant volumes of water';[37] one would have thought, therefore, that undershot wheels would not have been good for the Swere, a shallow river with a volume of water that varies dramatically from season to season.

Greater efficiency was achieved with the overshot wheel. Powered by water striking the top of the wheel, the overshot wheel needed 'a regulated water-supply, commonly collected in a mill pond from rivers and springs, then delivered through a sluice to a mill-race and chute properly set for the correct impact of the water on the wheel'.[38] Such a wheel may have driven the mill at Little Barford.

Before the work of John Smeaton (inventor/engineer), it had always been assumed that all wheels worked with the same efficiency, that the only variables were the volume and fall of water. Smeaton showed, by meticulous research, that the undershot wheel, which had come into more general use by the eighteenth century, had a maximum efficiency of 22%, and the overshot had a maximum efficiency of 63%. Smeaton's work led to the development of the breast-shot water-wheel which had a higher efficiency than any wheel so far employed, and was adopted at Paper Mill on Adderbury Grounds Farm, Deddington parish, where it is stored today. The highest efficiency was achieved – by the application of science to technology – on the eve of the extinction of the wheel's utility to society.

If we walk along the Swere from its source, we find mill houses have a modern life, with all necessary amenities, at Priory Mill, Wigginton, South Newington, Barford St Michael and Deddington; at other sites – Swerford and Milcombe – the mill houses have vanished. Exceptionally, the mill house on Adderbury Grounds Farm still stands, and its wheel is in place. It could turn again, or be repaired as an exhibition of a working mill on the River Swere.

Each mill was a considerable work of civil engineering, on a scale exceeded in England's rural places only by the building of canals and railways. The upper leat is an earthwork elevated more than a metre above the valley floor, a canal built to carry the river in a straight and unimpeded course to the mill in all seasons. Once the work is done, the water is carried away from the mill in the lower leat, usually for a much shorter distance than its advance to the mill, and rejoins the river from which it has been briefly diverted. The map on page 139 shows the upper leat advancing, for a long distance, toward the mill (site) at Barford St Michael; on the same map is shown a portion of the river in its original channel, some way to the north of the leat. The mill pond and the canalized river are new habitats, attractive to herbaceous species of still and slowly moving water.

If, in the early Middle Ages, 50 households were served by one mill, then nine mills on the Swere would have ground the corn for 450 households. Assuming there were five persons per household, each Swere mill would have served about 2,250 people. On the other hand, any mill might have developed a market wider than the local village for ground corn. In the earliest period, the mills would have ground relatively little wheat, for the standard fare of the Anglo-Saxon diet was rye, barley, oats, millet, beans and peas. A coarse meal was made of rye mixed with other grains, providing loaves for England's agricultural population.

Ownership of Corn- and Fulling-Mills

Mills were one of the most enduring capital assets of the rural economy. Penny Carey's research, transcribing the wills of mill-owners at South Newington and Milcombe, has made it possible to see how mills changed hands. From 1086 to 1357 we have no record of the South Newington mills, but, by the later date, the mill was ruinous, quite possibly as a result of rural depopulation following the Black Death. Optimism took hold in 1368 when the mill was leased to a miller from Bloxham. From the will of John Kinge, who died in 1628, we know that he was a fuller – the mill was probably both a corn- and fulling-mill by 1624. It is surely evidence of rural prosperity that by 1694 one John King 'devised to his grandson John French the mills next to his house in South Newington and all his other mills in the parish'. There were certainly three mills in South Newington confirmed by the terms of the sale of 'two fulling mills and a water corn mill' in 1757, although we do not know if these were in separate buildings, on separate sites or were double mills within the same building. By 1816 there was only one corn-mill and then, in the 1920s, the property became a private home.

Milcombe Mill is first known to us as a source of annual revenue for the Count of Evreux and Alfric in 1086. By the fourteenth century, the mill belonged to Eynsham Abbey and was let to tenants. One imagines a mill is always the property of a local farmer, at least a local resident, but this perhaps is less often the case. Milcombe Mill passed to a London draper in 1547. As late as 1800, water power – for England was blessed with rivers – greatly exceeded steam power. Many industrial activities – fulling, wood-turning, nail-making and iron-making – were water powered. But by 1850 the steam engine was grinding corn; water-mills were quickly disabled, and became the eyesores of a rural life in decline. Julian Barbour,

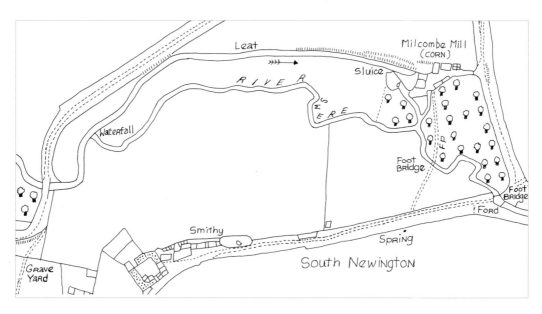

The River Swere divides just after the Banbury Road bridge, sending a leat to the Milcombe Mill, then derelict; the river loops through a farm meadow, and then the two streams reunite before crossing the ford in South Newington. Redrawn from the OS 1882 map.

Left: Amphibious bistort (*Persicaria amphibia*). This is an unusual plant as it has a terrestrial as well as an aquatic form, hence 'amphibious'. Here the stems are floating; the plant roots at the nodes, accounting for its density and mat-forming propensity. The Swere suits it here only because the river has slowed down, temporarily caught in the deep, still mill pond.

Below: A clutch of derelict buildings, at the site of Little Barford Mill, forms a stopping point and a moment of reverie for the walker along the footpath by the leat. The canalized river carries its deep solemn load to the ancient mill pond, and then, without turning a water-wheel, spills the water pellmell through a sluice gate, whereupon the river resumes its meandering course.

of South Newington, remembers the mill still working in the mid-1940s, when he was a boy; later the watercourses were filled in and the mill house was demolished.

Aubrey Charles, who worked at Milcombe Mill when he was a lad, remembers the big steam engines passing through on the road to Banbury Fair, stopping near the bridge over the Swere near the Milcombe leat. The drivers threw their pipes down into the mill stream to pump water into their boilers. He remembers they blew their whistles very loudly, the sound carried far and they were answered by other steam engines further up the road. (Records gathered by Penny Carey, of South Newington.)

Plant Life at Little Barford Mill

When first the river enters the alluvial plain of Barford St John, it meanders in a leisurely fashion; but then, where the river was made straight and high-banked on one side, it looks like a canal and, like a canal, the water is deep and slow. This change in depth and rate of flow favours a different flora. Common duckweed (*Lemna minor*) forms even larger colonies in the head pond. In the mill pond, darkening its depths, is curly waterweed (*Lagarosiphon major*) and perfoliate pondweed (*Potamogeton perfoliatus*), a native plant which occurs at only one other site in the Swere. In the nearly still water, slowly approaching the mill pond, is the river's largest stand of amphibious bistort (*Persicaria amphibia*). *Persicaria* is a far-creeping rhizomatous perennial. 'Amphibious' because it may grow on land too, in water-filled wheel-ruts of a farm vehicle, for example, but it looks most luxurious on the water surface. There is butterbur (*Petasites hybridus*) on the bank of the mill pond, but its occurrence is not related to the character of the canal-river.

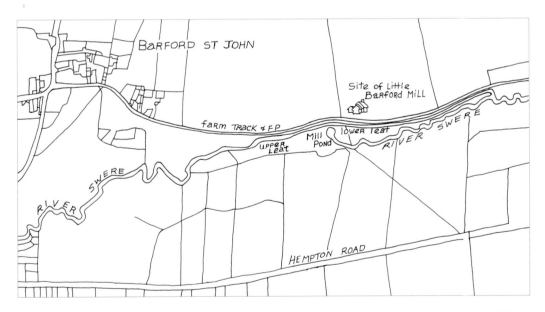

The river meanders across a field in sight of the hamlet of Barford St John, and then, when the channel has been straightened, a farm track runs by its side. Notice how, after leaving the mill pond, the river meanders ambitiously on towards Deddington.

Herbaceous Species on the Riverside West and East of the Little Barford Mill Pond

Plants West of the Mill Pond

Species of the Muddy Edges
Fool's-water-cress (*Apium nodiflorum*)
Hard Rush (*Juncus inflexus*)
Reed Sweet-grass (*Glyceria maxima*)
Water-cress (*Rorippa nasturtium-aquaticum*)
Water Forget-me-not (*Myosotis scorpioides*)

Species of the Banks
Great Willowherb (*Epilobium hirsutum*)
Water Figwort (*Scrophularia auriculata*)
Wild Teasel (*Dipsacus fullonum*)

Plants East of the Mill Pond

Aquatic Species
Common Duckweed (*Lemna minor*)
Yellow Water-lily (*Nuphar lutea*)

Emergent Species
Branched Bur-reed (*Sparganium erectum*)
Reed Canary-grass (*Phalaris arundinacea*)

Species of the Muddy Edges
Brooklime (*Veronica beccabunga*)
Fool's-water-cress (*Apium nodiflorum*)
Reed Sweet-grass (*Glyceria maxima*)
Water Forget-me-not (*Myosotis scorpioides*)

Species of the Banks
Gypsywort (*Lycopus europaeus*)
Great Willowherb (*Epilobium hirsutum*)
Marsh Thistle (*Cirsium palustre*)
Meadowsweet (*Filipendula ulmaria*)
Purple-loosestrife (*Lythrum salicaria*)
Welted Thistle (*Carduus crispus*)
Wild Angelica (*Angelica sylvestris*)
Wild Teasel (*Dipsacus fullonum*)

Top: A frosty winter scene where the River Swere is meandering from Barford St John. Two swans – are they feeding? – in the foreground. **Bottom:** The river straightened to form the upper leat, with reed sweet-grass (*Glyceria maxima*) on its edges, moves slowly towards the site of Little Barford Mill.

By the mill pond there are a derelict building, a sluice and an impressive spillway, history's thumbprint in the Swere valley. Once the river is released from its labour as a canal, it resumes meandering and accepts the company of alders (*Alnus glutinosa*) on its banks. Other trees – ash, a hawthorn, a sycamore – occur only occasionally. Regularly spaced and nearly equal in frequency to alder are old pollard willows (*Salix fragilis*).

Reed sweet-grass (*Glyceria maxima*) dominates the river banks of the upper leat – sheep grazing the banks create sloping muddy shores for the plant's rooting – and is not less common below the head pond where the river meanders and narrows. It grows out into the middle of the stream and slows its passage; yellow water-lilies (*Nuphar lutea*) grow beneath an overhanging ash (*Fraxinus excelsior*), and further along there is a dense stand of gypsywort (*Lycopus europaeus*). In March 2003, we saw moorhens, mallards and three tits – blue, great and long-tailed.

Domesday Book Water-Mills of the River Swere

1. Priory Mill (SP 333 299)

First mill on the Swere, with a large storage pond, now an ornament to the private seventeenth-century house; the Chipping Norton Steam Granary operated here in the 1930s, then the mill fell into disrepair.

2. Swerford (SP 375 313)

The mill building no longer exists.

3. Wigginton (SP 391 330)

In 1851, a 'miller continued to work the water-grist-mill until at least 1920';[39] now a private house with a lively mill pond below the sluice.

4. South Newington (SP 406 334)

Now a private house.

5. Milcombe Mill (SP 411 335)

The mill house, with stone mullions, was demolished; some barns and supporting buildings remain.

6. Barford St Michael (SP 434 328)

Was the mill of the manor; has date stones – activity recorded for 1717, 1762, 1812; now a private house.

7. Barford St John (SP 446 331)

Called Little Barford Mill on one map; the smallest mill working on the Swere, work done by a farmer rather than a miller; large head pond; machinery still on site.

8. Deddington (SP 455 329)

Now a private house; some gear still in place.

9. Adderbury Grounds (SP 470 352)

The history of this mill – the last on the Swere – is more fully recorded in the VCH than any of the other mills on the Swere.

Left: Wild teasel (*Dipsacus fullonum*). A cultivated variety of teasel was used to raise the nap of woollen cloth in the manufacture of fabrics such as velour and cashmere. Its spines curve back, forming hooks, and these are more stiff than those of the wild species, the better to pull the wool. Teasel is in the Dipsacaceae family, but closely resembles the compound flower of the Asteraceae, with its prickly stem and spiny bracts extending well past the small lilac flowers.

Below: The weir at South Newington. It was here, when the weir was repaired in 1999, that 57 white-clawed crayfish were caught and removed to other parts of the Swere by the Environment Agency. The weir diverts water flowing in the upper leat from making any further approach to the mill, long disused, and sends it back to the river from whence it came.

The Old Paper Mill, Adderbury Grounds Farm. Standing free of a private dwelling, this mill is in moderately good structural repair; the wheel is put away, but it could turn again. The photograph has been taken standing back along the course of the lower leat, looking towards the mill house. The brickwork of the arched space is covered with the largest population of maidenhair spleenwort (*Asplenium trichomanes*) found anywhere along the Swere, walls and crevices of mainly basic rocks being this fern's preferred habitat.

BULRUSH MARSHES

THE PAIUTE INDIANS of the Great Basin of Nevada mashed the rhizomes of bulrushes to make bread, and used the new shoots and pollen too. There were several tribes of Paiutes, one of which was called the Bulrush Eaters. 'Spring was a good time. It meant that the new shoots of the bulrush would soon appear above the water. Women waded into the marshes, reaching arm-deep into the chilly water to search in the mud.' The white spears were cleaned and passed to the hungry children. There were other uses too: the long, slender, flat leaves were braided and twisted, woven and matted, made into twine, bedding and blankets.[40]

Common bulrush is *Typha latifolia*; its cousin, lesser bulrush, is *T. angustifolia*. Both species are tall: 1.5-2.5 m for *Typha latifolia* and not more than 2 m for *T. angustifolia*. The long, slender, slightly curving, soft green leaves give both plants their exceptional beauty, adding an attractive feature to a garden pond. Bulrushes are also called 'cat's-tails', more in America than in the UK. Here, bulrushes are also called reedmaces. Stands of cat's-tails are

Common bulrush (*Typha latifolia*). When the fully ripe fruiting head is shaken, the seeds set sail on the vagrant wind. With luck, some are carried to a habitat of the plant's liking – places where rich silts gather in lakes, canals, rivers and reed-swamps. This photograph shows clearly that the slender male flowers stand immediately above the female flowers; this is not true of lesser bulrush (*T. angustifolia*), where on the stem the sexes are more separated.

usually dense, even congested, because the plants spread by vegetative propagation – indeed, they are stout rhizomatous herbs – and if they are planted in a pond, they will surely increase and multiply.

In wetland habitats along the River Swere, bulrushes occur in some places without forming the dominant plant community. There is a dense stand of *Typha latifolia* at the southeast corner of Clearwater Pond, where two bodies of fresh water – a spring and a stream – flow together. Here the water is richly oxygenated. Bulrushes are able to grow in deep water, but are at a disadvantage in shallow water, particularly in seasons when the water-table drops below the soil surface. What is of interest here is that a '*T. angustifolia* swamp is rare' in Oxfordshire, but not along the Swere.[41] In 29 Swere ponds and marshes, common bulrush occurs at nine sites, including one site on the northern tributary; lesser bulrush occurs at four sites and is dominant in one of these, at The Scrapes, Barford St John. These species, looking so similar in many ways, seldom occur together, the reason being that each has a habitat tolerance not shared by the other. For example, it is thought that lesser bulrush, which is dominant in the most shallow pond of the stillest water, is more tolerant of lower levels of oxygen. The Scrapes is interesting because there the bulrush stand gives way to a sub-community of water mint (*Mentha aquatica*), a reflection of the changing water-table.

Species Associated with *Typha* in the Bulrush Marshes

	Typha latifolia	Typha angustifolia
Common Spike-rush (*Eleocharis palustris*)	✗	✓
Fool's-water-cress (*Apium nodiflorum*)	✓	✗
Gypsywort (*Lycopus europaeus*)	✗	✓
Great Willowherb (*Epilobium hirsutum*)	✓	✗
Jointed Rush (*Juncus articulatus*)	✗	✓
Lesser Pond-sedge (*Carex acutiformis*)	✓	✗
Marsh Thistle (*Cirsium palustre*)	✓	✗
Meadowsweet (*Filipendula ulmaria*)	✓	✗
Purple-loosestrife (*Lythrum salicaria*)	✗	✓
Reed Canary-grass (*Phalaris arundinacea*)	✗	✓
Ribwort Plantain (*Plantago lanceolata*)	✗	✓
Soft-rush (*Juncus inflexus*)	✓	✗
Tufted Hair-grass (*Deschampsia cespitosa*)	✗	✓
Water Forget-me-not (*Myosotis scorpioides*)	✓	✓
Water Mint (*Mentha aquatica*)	✗	✓
Water-plantain (*Alisma plantago-aquatica*)	✗	✓
Yellow Iris (*Iris pseudacorus*)	✗	✓
Wild Angelica (*Angelica sylvestris*)	✓	✓

Of the 18 species in the table above, only water forget-me-not (*Myosotis scorpioides*) and wild angelica (*Angelica sylvestris*) occur in association with each *Typha* species.

THE SCRAPES

A MILL STONE, or quern, leans absent-mindedly against the wall of the old mill at Barford St Michael, now a private residence. A few steps away, a handsome footbridge joins the two Barfords over the Swere. Here the river is wide and deep, and the water moves swiftly. Pools of light filter through the tree canopy, diminishing the darkness spread over the stream by alder (*Alnus glutinosa*) and sycamore (*Acer pseudoplatanus*) which crowd the bank. On the Barford St John side, there are plantings of guelder-rose (*Viburnum opulus*) and wayfaring-tree (*V. lantana*) by a bench. A clayey footpath, along which one slips and slides in the wet season, leads to a site where two pools were dug by Robin Woolgrove, called The Scrapes. The plan was to let nature take its course, which it did: a passing breeze posted bulrush seeds, and the ornamental pools became lesser bulrush (*Typha angustifolia*) marshes. On the outer edge of the marsh are tussocks of tufted hair-grass (*Deschampsia cespitosa*), monumental in size and structure. Water mint (*Mentha aquatica*), a low-growing plant able to tolerate lower levels of water than *Typha angustifolia*, fills the spaces between the bulrushes.

The footbridge over the River Swere to The Scrapes, Barford St John.

Top left: Alder (*Alnus glutinosa*) and sycamore (*Acer pseudoplatanus*) trees on the river bank.
Top right: A guelder-rose (*Viburnum opulus*), in fruit. **Bottom left:** One of The Scrapes pools.
Bottom right: Summer reveals the dominance of lesser bulrush (*Typha angustifolia*).

GREAT TREES AND WOODED EDGES

WOODED EDGES line the river banks and are often continuous for long distances, especially in the upper course of the river, but they become infrequent below Paradise Farm and are more occasional and patchy from Wigginton to the River Cherwell. The Dingle is an exception, a tiny space with a few great trees; above and to its east is a dense understorey thicket.

As in overgrown hedges, there are spindly shrubs – sometimes interlocked – and canopy-sized trees. Field maple (*Acer campestre*) and hazel (*Corylus avellana*) are frequent where the river is criss-crossed with branches west of Swerford village, the only part of the river that seems an escape from civilized society. In this same reach, hazel may grow to 6.5 m where grey willow (*Salix cinerea*) is dominant and common hawthorn (*Crataegus monogyna*), elder (*Sambucus nigra*) and wayfaring-tree (*Viburnum lantana*) are occasional.

London plane (*Platanus* x *hispanica*). In great cities, like Philadelphia, there are avenues of London plane trees, for they are not only handsome but tolerant of car exhaust fumes. The leaves are vast, 12–25 cm, with triangular lobes, and the bark is dull white and light brown. On the lawn of Barford Manor, these London plane trees are a monument to longevity.

While great trees of the riverside are rare, like Chelsea pensioners they are cherished and admired for their longevity: sycamores (*Acer pseudoplatanus*) planted on the motte at Swerford castle grounds, for example, are of a great age, as are the London plane (*Platanus* x *hispanica*) trees in the grounds of Barford Manor, and a sweet chestnut (*Castanea sativa*) on the river edge in The Dingle.

Map of The Dingle (SP 425 335).

The river edge has grown unserviceable to farmers: hazel is not harvested, willow is rarely pollarded and tinder is uncollected. In fact, being a treed river edge is itself a sign of neglect. In some places, the Milcombe valley, for example, there are trees today where in 1882, as shown on the OS map of that year, the river edge was treeless. After all, tree limbs break and fall into the water, clogging the channel, and induce the land to flood. After high winds in October 2002, seven of ten crack-willow (*Salix fragilis*) trees in one stretch along the river in the Milcombe valley had their main trunks broken; they laid the foundations of a naturally constructed otter's holt and provided an aerial bridge for brave children to cross from one side of the river to the other.

An excellent wooded edge is towards Wigginton from Between Towns Road, Swerford. Ash (*Fraxinus excelsior*), beech (*Fagus sylvatica*), English oak (*Quercus robur*), field maple, red oak (*Q. rubra*), sycamore and four walnut (*Juglans regia*) trees grow on the edge. Blackthorn (*Prunus spinosa*) (5 m high), buckthorn (*Rhamnus cathartica*), common hawthorn, elder, hazel and honeysuckle (*Lonicera periclymenum*) form the shrub storey; climbers include blackberry (*Rubus fruticosus*), dog-rose (*Rosa canina*) and field-rose (*R. arvensis*). The beech, red oak and walnut trees are not self-sown. Here, as in all the places by the river, man ornaments the landscape and the trees are a combination of 'wild' and artifice.

Great Trees by the River Swere:

Top left: Sycamore (*Acer pseudoplatanus*). The only motte and bailey overlooking the Swere stands below the Swerford village church. Ringing the motte, and near the summit of its banks, are the most splendid specimens of sycamore, a tree that grows to 30 m and has a broad spreading crown. Introduced during the Tudor monarchy, sycamore is naturalized in the British Isles.

Top right: The characteristic twisted bark of sweet chestnut, also called Spanish chestnut (*Castanea sativa*). This large tree, the only sweet chestnut beside the River Swere, stands proudly on the small flat riverside space called The Dingle. Perhaps it was planted in the same era as the great English oak (*Quercus robur*) that stands nearby. The oak, fractured and broken, was struck in the wild storm of October 2002, but the chestnut was spared. An even larger sweet chestnut stands before the manor house at Rousham, and shows a little more clearly than The Dingle tree a pattern of its bark: longitudinal fissures which do not run straight up and down, but curve to the right. Like sycamore, sweet chestnut is an introduction to the British Isles, and is extensively naturalized in South East England.

Bottom left and right: English or pedunculate oak (*Quercus robur*). This is a tree which almost everyone calls English oak. But, what is a peduncle? It is the stalk of a flower, and hence of an acorn. In contrast, the sessile oak (*Q. petraea*), which does not occur along the Swere, has no peduncle. What grips our attention, in considering *Q. robur*, is its girth, its height, the massive serpentine branches, the wide shade the tree casts, its stubborn trait in holding on to its leaves long into the autumn and its parsimony in greeting spring.
Left, in The Dingle, is an English oak snapped in half by the storm of October 2002; to the **right** is an English oak, showing its characteristic form. Uncommon on calcareous soils, *Q. robur* is more often found on clay soil, one reason that it is a common riverside tree in Deddington parish between Deddington Mill and Bloxham Bridge.

OAK FIELD MARSHES

THESE FIELD MARSHES are *Juncus* marshes, wetland dominated by soft-rush (*Juncus effusus*) or hard rush (*J. inflexus*). In rush marshes, individual plants stand farther apart from one another whereas sedge marshes are more congested. *Juncus* marshes occur in seasonally wet to spongy places with poor drainage of surface water, whereas in sedge marshes ground water gathers and is held for a longer time.

Oak Field Marshes

Oak Field Marshes, in Barford St Michael parish, are bordered by a footpath that connects Barford St Michael to places upriver. Three fields lie along the river; no one is greatly different from another. In effect, they form a single marshland of variously moist and dry ground in which a variety of wetland species are unevenly distributed. The footpath, passing first by

A line of English oak (*Quercus robur*) trees clearly marks dry ground. The land rises, sweeping up to the left, showing fields recently harvested, whereas the field marsh, with seed set on the tall slender marsh thistles (*Cirsium palustre*) – cottony tufts atop erect green stems – extends towards the camera from the sanctuary of the oak trees.

splendid old English oak trees (*Quercus robur*) and shown on the OS 191 map to be on the eastern side of the hedgerow, links all the fields. The oak trees are a boundary; they stand just above the edge of the marsh fields, where the land begins to sweep up in an attractive formation. No single species dominates these marshes. Each spring-fed field is its own bouquet of herbs, with some species locally dominant. The size of the fields – each 3–5 ha – is striking, if one had become used to the narrow valleys above Wigginton. The Barfords mark the middle course of the river, with wide fields and meadows. Among the many locally dominant plants are two species of St John's-wort (*Hypericum maculatum* and *H. tetrapterum*), and wild angelica (*Angelica sylvestris*), but in none of the wide spaces is meadowsweet, rush or sedge dominant over the whole area.

Greater bird's-foot-trefoil (*Lotus pedunculatus*). Native to damp grassy places throughout the British Isles, this member of the bean family (Fabaceae) grows in dense patches in the Oak Field Marshes, but its density (and dominance) is purely local. Such densities are characteristic of many species spreading more by vegetative growth, in this case by stolons, than sexual reproduction.

The river is relatively straight where it forms the continuous western border of the Oak Field Marshes, but at the northern end, where a plank bridge composed of railway sleepers and telegraph poles crosses the river, it meanders zealously, like a dancer who, after a period of restraint, has been permitted to dance once more. From the plank bridge, and towards South Newington, the riverside is wooded, whereas in the Barford valley there is only a dotting of trees, crack-willow (*Salix fragilis*) more than alder (*Alnus glutinosa*). The Oak Field Marshes species are listed below.

Top: A swan on the glass-green surface of the old manorial moat, Barford St Michael. These waters are also frequently visited by Canada geese. **Bottom:** The Swere runs in a fairly straight channel, the full length of Oak Field Marshes, and then the river is divided. The roiling water in this photograph is the mill stream; with greater calm and solemnity the river proper continues its way east, past Mill Lane, The Scrapes and the handsome bridge at the site of the old ford between the Barfords.

Herbaceous Species of Oak Field Marshes

Bearded Couch (*Elymus caninus*)

Compact Rush (*Juncus conglomeratus*)

Creeping Buttercup (*Ranunculus repens*)

Great Willowherb (*Epilobium hirsutum*)

Greater Bird's-foot-trefoil (*Lotus pedunculatus*)

Hard Rush (*Juncus inflexus*)

Imperforate St John's-wort (*Hypericum maculatum*)

Jointed Rush (*Juncus articulatus*)

Marsh Thistle (*Cirsium palustre*)

Meadowsweet (*Filipendula ulmaria*)

Perforate St John's-wort (*Hypericum perforatum*)

Purple-loosestrife (*Lythrum salicaria*)

Reed Canary-grass (*Phalaris arundinacea*)

Sedge (*Carex sp.*)

Soft-rush (*Juncus effusus*)

Square-stalked St John's-wort (*Hypericum tetrapterum*)

Tufted Hair-grass (*Deschampsia cespitosa*)

Water Figwort (*Scrophularia auriculata*)

Water Mint (*Mentha aquatica*)

Wild Angelica (*Angelica sylvestris*)

Wood Dock (*Rumex sanguineus*)

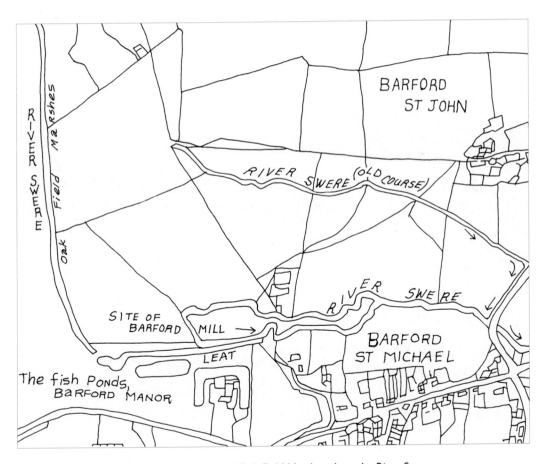

Map showing the siting of Oak Field Marshes along the River Swere.

LANDSCAPE PASTORALE: EAST OF LITTLE BARFORD MILL

THERE ARE PLACES along the river where one feels, 'This is perfect!' It is an aesthetic judgement, influenced by painting, the history of landscape and one's sense of well-being. East from Barford St John, the river is a storyline with varied incidents. The hamlet and its tiny church retain a reticent regard for our progress. Horses – rare enough along the riverway – suggest the use of pasture no longer claimed for the dairy herd. Prairie-like fields, unlike any west or east of Little Barford Mill, swoop up and across the entire landscape from the site of the decayed corn-mill; above the hill a buzzard lingers mid-air as if on a kite string. To the

The river east of Little Barford Mill. Reed sweet-grass (*Glyceria maxima*) clutters its margins; the water is nearly still, tall trees of Deddington Mill line the back of the photograph and cattle graze in the wide valley between the river and the wood.

Yellow water-lily (*Nuphar lutea*).

mill from Barford St John, the river has been contained in a narrow channel; now it splashes down from the sluice gate, whirls in a pool, regains its poise and becomes the meandering Swere again.

Reed sweet-grass (*Glyceria maxima*) is dominant along the margins of the river advancing to the mill; east of Little Barford Mill its prosperity continues, but as the river advances towards Deddington parish, reed sweet-grass becomes less abundant. Sheep feed eagerly on a grass that has always been known to farmers as 'highly productive and palatable ... once much prized as a fodder.'[42] *Glyceria* forms a dense and luxuriant growth, sometimes choking oxbows or narrow channels where banks shelve gently into the watercourse. Dense stands detach themselves from moorings on the river edge and become floating islets of vegetation. New shoots push up during the long growing season, then the leaves die back rapidly in November, becoming brown and down-bent, adding another source of organic richness to the ancient stream.

Yellow water-lily (*Nuphar lutea*) grows in this stretch of the river, but nowhere above Little Barford Mill. The full development of the large plants requires deep water. Also favouring *Nuphar*'s growth is standing or slowly moving water. For the first time these two conditions have been met in the Swere; what seems merely the chance appearance of a beautiful flower, which contributes so much to the beauty of this stretch of the river, is an effect of a change in the river's depth and rate of flow. As a wide sluggish stream, the Swere seems to be on holiday.

TANTALIZING BUTTERFLIES

BUTTERFLIES are creatures of tantalizing beauty. Their every movement, even the slow opening and folding of the wings, is alluring. Elusive in flight, butterflies seem to flutter for our pleasure. In tropical jungles, men have endured disease and lethargy to hunt, capture, kill and exhibit a Morpho in a glass box. We now know better.

Butterflies have their own urgencies quite apart from our daydreams. Fluttering flight, for example, allows them to distract and elude avian predators, and a youth's butterfly net. Adults live only a short while, not more than a single summer, and in that time each butterfly must find a mate. As in our own lives, weather too is a constraint; for butterflies generally refuse to fly on cold or wet days. Male flight patterns are recognition signals to females of the same species. Surprisingly, butterflies gather at special sites – an opening in a wood, a sunny spot by a river, a rock – sites visited generation after generation, serving the same function as a youth club or disco, for the sexes to meet. Later, the female must find the right plant on which to lay her eggs.

The Clouded Yellow (*Colias croceus*) butterfly. Notice the eye dot on the lower wing, the large green eye on the head and the long antenna with the characteristic knob on the end.

In providing a food source for the larvae, there is a remarkable specificity in selecting the host plant. Other species are less choosy. Eggs are laid one at a time, glued to the underside of a leaf. The Brimstone (*Gonepteryx rhamni*), for example, selects the leaves and buds of buckthorn (*Rhamnus cathartica*); the Small Copper (*Lycaena phlaeas*), frequenting Swere valleys, chooses docks and sorrel; Red Admiral (*Vanessa atalanta*) searches for common nettle (*Urtica dioica*).

Left: Brimstone (*Gonepteryx rhamni*). **Right:** Peacock (*Inachis io*).

Left: Gatekeeper (*Pyronia tithonus*). **Right:** Comma (*Polygonia c'album*).

Consider the consequences of a mistaken identification. Some butterfly larvae are programmed to feed on only one plant species; hatched on the wrong plant, they refuse to feed, and die of starvation. Species that are not choosy do not have this problem. The other possibility is that the larvae die of plant poison. Plants commonly defend themselves against insect herbivory by concentrating one or more toxins in their leaves. Some butterfly species are immune to particular toxins, and may even make use of them for their own defence. The Monarch butterfly (*Danaus plexippus*) of North America is immune to the milkweed (*Asclepias syriaca*) toxin; more surprisingly, the adult butterfly is able to retain the toxin in its own body with the result that birds, after a first taste, avoid making a meal of any more Monarchs.

How impossible it is to believe that a caterpillar – greedy, fat and hairy – is the youth of an adult butterfly, an insect of elaborate but light-winged beauty, one that sips nectar rather than devastates leaves. For this employment the long slender proboscis is perfectly adapted. Which came first, a long tongue or a tubular corolla? Adults usually drink from a wide range of flowers, and therewith provide pollination services to many species. Nectar is never toxic but it is always an attractant, inducing butterflies to become vectors of pollination. In this way they are contributing to the propagation of a plant species that feeds them.

We expect birds to migrate, to elect not to face winter when food supplies are diminished and the hazard of predation is increased, but it is a surprise to find that the Clouded Yellow (*Colias croceus*) and the Red Admiral winter in southern Europe; the Painted Lady (*Vanessa cardui*), venturing farther away, winters in North Africa.

Butterfly-rich habitats along the Swere are flowery meadows, especially in the Swere Bank SSSI, and in the old hay meadows of the Wigginton and Milcombe valleys. Flowers adapted to pollination by butterflies are chiefly blue or deep pink. Marsh and meadow plants from along the Swere that are listed as 'among flowers most visited by British Lepidoptera'[43]

A Large Skipper (*Ochlodes venata*).

include: common fleabane (*Pulicaria dysenterica*), devil's-bit scabious (*Succisa pratensis*), hemp-agrimony (*Eupatorium cannabinum*), knapweed (*Centaurea* sp.), ragged-Robin (*Lychnis flos-cuculi*), thistle (*Cirsium* sp.) and wild teasel (*Dipsacus fullonum*).

We had not thought of butterflies, when we first set out in the autumn of 2002 to walk along the Swere, but in the warm summer following, they presented themselves in such beauty and some species in such numbers that they would not be deprived of our full attention. It has been estimated that the regularly occurring butterfly fauna of the British Isles includes 60 species; we saw 22 species, or about 37% of the regulars.

Butterflies Seen in the Swere Valley

Brimstone (*Gonepteryx rhamni*)	Meadow Brown (*Maniola jurtina*)
Brown Argus (*Aricia agestis*)	Orange Tip (*Anthocharis cardamines*)
Clouded Yellow (*Colias croceus*)	Painted Lady (*Vanessa cardui*)
Comma (*Polygonia c'album*)	Peacock (*Inachis io*)
Common Blue (*Polyommatus icarus*)	Red Admiral (*Vanessa atalanta*)
Gatekeeper (*Pyronia tithonus*)	Ringlet (*Aphantopus hyperantus*)
Green-veined White (*Pieris napi*)	Small Copper (*Lycaena phlaeas*)
Holly Blue (*Celastrina argiolus*)	Small Skipper (*Thymelicus sylvestris*)
Large Skipper (*Ochlodes venata*)	Small Tortoiseshell (*Aglais urticae*)
Large White (*Pieris brassicae*)	Small White (*Pieris rapae*)
Marbled White (*Melanargia galathea*)	Speckled Wood (*Pararge aegeria*)

The list above is no indication of the abundance of the different species, which vary greatly, but a record of what can be done when one has an interest, and the knowledge and patience to pursue it.

Purple-loosestrife (*Lythrum salicaria*), wild teasel (*Dipsacus fullonum*) and common fleabane (*Pulicaria dysenterica*).

BY DAEDA'S WOOD

DAEDA'S WOOD is a story of community action for the conservation of trees. 'Ancient woods' are 'those which have had a continuous woodland cover since at least AD 1600 and have only been cleared for understorey or timber production'. In 'the Cherwell Valley ... no wood at all is recorded for most of the villages except on the east of the river from Islip down'.[44] Deddington is typical of Cherwell Valley villages, a landscape from which trees were felled long before the Parliamentary Enclosure Act of 1808, and in which nearly all of the land was put to agricultural use. In our time, Daeda's Wood has reversed this trend.

Bloxham Bridge, on the Milton Gated Road, was built by James Hopcraft, mason, in 1859. Looking down from this bridge, we spotted the only site along the River Swere of a fern called wall-rue (*Asplenium ruta-muraria*). It was growing, as one expects it to, on the ledge above the brick arch.

The Woodland Trust sponsored the planting of 3,500 trees in 1996 on a 3.68 ha field – now called Daeda's Wood – along the River Swere, part of the Woods-On-Your-Doorstep project. Today, the smallest saplings are strapping youths. Ronald Canning, of Deddington, when a boy in the 1930s, remembers that his grandfather and sons farmed the two water

Above: Before Daeda's Wood, summer 1996, looking on to the field where the trees and shrubs were going to be planted. **Below:** A portion of the same field in July, 1999.

meadows where the Millennium Wood has now been developed. The meadows were not so wet they could not be used for grazing and haymaking in the late summer. Our photograph of the site shows a field of grain – a change of policy between Ronald's boyhood and the early post-war years. During periods of heavy rain, the river flooded in the 1930s, as it does today, but less often. Ronald remembers that riverside 'crack-willows were cut back during the winter to provide materials for post-and-rails and for making hurdles which were used for penning sheep. Trunks would sometimes split and fall to the ground, so woe betide anyone who was in the way.' Old crack-willows (*Salix fragilis*), torn open and leaning over, are a feature of the river's edge in Daeda's Wood. Sycamore (*Acer pseudoplatanus*) is dominant in both Daeda's Wood and Hazel Wood near Bloxham Bridge.

In August, the reckless hurry of the winter water is hushed by summer drought. Broad-bodied Chasers (*Libellula depressa*) and Ruddy Darters (*Sympetrum sanguineum*), with broad wings fixed in extension, hunt over the water where, mid-stream, there are dense stands of branched bur-reed (*Sparganium erectum*), patches of arrowhead (*Sagittaria sagittifolia*) and white water-lily (*Nymphaea alba*). On the river's edge, great willowherb (*Epilobium hirsutum*) and reed canary-grass (*Phalaris arundinacea*) conceal the summit of the banks. Tadpoles swim harum-scarum where common duckweed (*Lemna minor*) and common water-starwort (*Callitriche stagnalis*) grow in quiet bays near the shore. White water-lily is intolerant of turbidity, a condition it need not fear in the deep (1 m) still water beside Daeda's Wood in somnolent summer.

Along the river's edge of Hazel Wood, which is private property, neglect has been the father of wilderness: sycamore darkens the banks and old hazel (*Corylus avellana*) shrubs thrive on the floodplain, probably a relic of earlier farming practices. At the eastern end of Hazel Wood, light dispels mystery where the river straightens and runs an unbending course to Adderbury Bridge. At both sites, trees have been left to grow as they will, but, with newer initiatives, the look of the riverside may change and so, for the sake of a historical record, this list has been prepared.

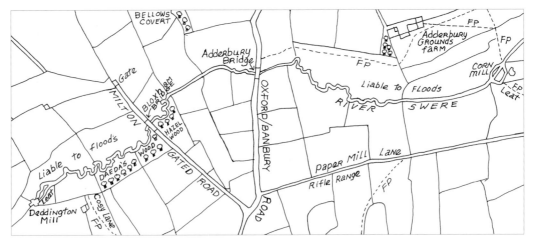

Map of the River Swere in Deddington parish.

The Woody Species of Daeda's Wood and Hazel Wood

	Daeda	Hazel
Apple (*Malus* agg.)	✗	✓
Ash (*Fraxinus excelsior*)	✓	✓
Aspen (*Populus tremula*)*	✗	✓
Beech (*Fagus sylvatica*)	✗	✓
Blackthorn (*Prunus spinosa*)	✓	✓
Common Hawthorn (*Crataegus monogyna*)	✓	✓
Crack-willow (*Salix fragilis*)	✓	✓
Elder (*Sambucus nigra*)	✓	✓
English Elm (*Ulmus procera*)	✓	✓
English Oak (*Quercus robur*)*	✓	✓
Hazel (*Corylus avellana*)	✗	✓
Sycamore (*Acer pseudoplatanus*)	✓	✓

Key: ✓ = present at site; ✗ = absent at site; * = planted recently.

Crab apple (*Malus* agg.). White petals suffused with pink, crab apple has a distinctly feminine beauty, but it is occasionally thorny and fits well into the fabric of a hedge with common hawthorn (*Crataegus monogyna*) and blackthorn (*Prunus spinosa*). The flowers, with nectaries on the receptacle, are pollinated by flies and wasps.

Top: Crack-willow (*Salix fragilis*). **Bottom:** The River Swere in Daeda's Wood.

Branched bur-reed (*Sparganium erectum*). The tall sword-like leaves (triangular in section) look like iris blades, but the flowers are distinctly different. The branching stems bear two kinds of flowers with the unopened male flowers above the larger heads of female flowers in full bloom below. Where the river moves slowly, and muds have gathered, this native plant easily takes root in the Swere.

Left: A male Broad-bodied Chaser (*Libellula depressa*); **Right:** A male Ruddy Darter (*Sympetrum sanguineum*) commonly seen near and over the River Swere in Daeda's Wood.

CRACK-WILLOW

CRACK-WILLOW (*Salix fragilis*) trees are picturesque in all presentations. Age itself and the exhibition of a rampant hardihood, despite setbacks, make this tree, more than any other, the wizard of the riverside wood. *Salix fragilis* has played many parts in the countryside, but its utility has lapsed; now we see trees either broken down, damaged or decayed, or needing to be pollarded. Some are kept up and have been pollarded recently, but these are the exception.

Crack-willow (*Salix fragilis*) trees, formerly pollarded, but now left to grow a thicket of branches.

Pollarding strengthens and preserves a tree; serving man and the farmer's interests increases its longevity. Typically, crack-willow trees live to be 200 years old, but 1,000 years are possible. The old wood may rot, but the tree stays alive; it may become hollow and shelter man or beast, and refuse to give way. A robust tree may grow as much as 2 cm a year in girth; eventually the bark is deeply fissured and the bole reaches a substantial size. New shoots grow quickly from the pollarded bole. When the tips of young twigs are ready, and it makes no difference how old or young the tree is, they break off easily and make a 'sharp crack' – hence '*fragilis*' in its Latin name. Falling into a passing stream, chance carries the twigs, either near or far, to a river bank where they will take root and sprout in the spring.

Top left: Storm damage of October 2002. **Top right:** Old pollards leaning over the Swere by Daeda's Wood. **Bottom left:** A splendid example of how a tree may grow without its heartwood. Crack-willows split open, even in the absence of great wind, exposing the heartwood which then decays; but the tree lives, its vascular cambium undamaged. John Evelyn, the seventeenth-century diarist, suggested collecting the crumblings from decaying heartwood for garden compost. **Bottom right:** Crack-willow as a porcupine. The crown becomes knobby with successive pollardings.

DRAGONS AND DAMSELS

D RAGONFLIES AND DAMSELFLIES are spectacular insects that are strongly associated with watery habitats. People often ask how can the two groups be distinguished. A short answer is that damselflies are smaller, and have slender bodies. Being lady-like, they rest with their wings closed; dragonflies rest with their wings open, and in this position their giant progenitors in the fossil history have been preserved. Once the wings are dry and fully

Above: Heron Pond. Ideal habitat for the Broad-bodied Chaser (*Libellula depressa*) which prefers hunting where the water is nearly still and deep, and ideal too for the carnivorous nymphs of both dragonflies and damselflies.

Right: Summer sightings of damselflies and dragonflies along the River Swere:
Broad-bodied Chaser (*Libellula depressa*), female; Southern Hawker (*Aeshna cyanea*), male; Common Blue Damselflies (*Enallagma cyathigerum*); Beautiful Demoiselle (*Calopterix virgo*), male; Ruddy Darter (*Sympetrum sanguineum*), female; Blue-tailed Damselfly (*Ischnura elegans*); Banded Demoiselles (*Calopterix splendens*); Ruddy Darter (*Sympetrum sanguineum*), male.

extended, they lock in position and cannot be closed. Both groups lay their eggs in water or on water plants, and these develop into nymphs which may live for up to two years in the pond or river. Like the adult insect, the nymph is carnivorous and will eat any small creatures that it can catch.

Dragonfly larvae are well-camouflaged; in hunting river fauna, they sit and wait for prey to come within striking range. A remarkable structure called the mask covers the mouth parts; it is a hinged unit with a pair of movable hooks. When prey is detected, the larva stalks slowly, the mask extends and impales the prey on the hooks and then folds back into position in one-fortieth of a second.

In shallow water with emergent plants, like rushes (*Juncus* sp.) or branched bur-reed (*Sparganium erectum*), the dragonfly nymph will climb out of the water, usually during the summer months, to allow the adult insect to emerge from its exoskeleton. Emergence is a slow process and can take several hours; during this time the insect is very vulnerable to predators, so it often takes place very early in the morning. As adults, dragonflies need to eat up to one-fifth of their body weight each day. The larger species catch mayflies, butterflies and even small damselflies.

Darter and Hawker Dragonflies have different ways of feeding. Darters perch on a branch that gives a wide field of vision and dart into the air when flying prey attracts their attention – not unlike the kingfisher, another airborne riverside hunter. Hawker Dragonflies 'patrol regular beats, often flying considerable distances from the ponds and rivers in which they breed. They take insects on the wing, using their powerful jaws to dismember prey, while holding it with their spiny legs.'[45]

The larger dragonflies will often have more extensive territories and spend a lot of time away from water. Hunting for prey on the wing, their large eyes constantly 'scan the forward visual field for prey' and at the same time the brain 'continuously monitors its airspeed, so that it knows if it has to decelerate to swoop on a slower insect or if it has to accelerate to bear down on a faster one.'[46]

Both damselflies and dragonflies adopt a tandem position when mating, seen in the photograph of the Common Blue Damselflies (*Enallagma cyathigerum*). Some damselflies keep the attached position during egg-laying, others flick the fertilized eggs into the water while the male protectively hovers above.

The River Swere has a good selection of both damselflies and dragonflies, but many occur only in particular areas. The Beautiful Demoiselle (*Calopterix virgo*), for example, prefers shallow, flowing water with a stony base, whereas the Banded Demoiselle (*Calopterix splendens*) likes slower, deeper water, as in ponds and canals. The Swere changes in just this way from its middle to lower course, and so the Banded Demoiselle dominates in the stretch from the Barfords to the confluence with the River Cherwell; the Beautiful Demoiselle rules from Swerford to South Newington.

Right: Good Banded Demoiselle country! The river east of Little Barford Mill, with water deep and slow.

WINTER ADVANCING

SUMMER IS EXPRESSED in tennis, cricket and afternoon picnics, rising pollen counts, Henley and Wimbledon, and hedges that heave with elder flowers. Slowly at first, but advancing steadily, nature's favours are withdrawn. Violent rainstorms break the spell of summer's drought; the lax river rises, flooding the meadows. Cold mist lingers long in the morning air, from which have disappeared low cruising swallows and high darting swifts. Only jackdaws, perennial village residents, keep watch from the golden weathervane on the church steeple.

The dairy cows are kept in more often now, and their diet is changed to Lenten rations; they will have to wait until Easter for fresh grass. Even for overwintering cattle, grazing is restricted, so that the best pasture and hayfields may be protected against puddling. Summer's harvest, which more and more is compressed into black plastic bags, is left in the field and not hurried into the dry of the barn.

Above: Swans on the 'canal' leading to Little Barford Mill.
Top right: Flooded fields near the confluence with the River Cherwell.
Bottom right: Winter feed in black plastic bags, along the farm track near Little Barford Mill.
The special beauty of a winter scene: frost sparkling in the grass, a season when brown becomes a colour of more varied contrasts, and slanting light glimmers on the sunny side of the trees.

Top: Where ground is well-drained, cows may be let on to the land, as the farmer has done below the motte and bailey castle of Swerford village.

Bottom: Kept out of doors in winter, sheep graze grasses more tightly than dairy cows or good beef stock and may stay corralled in winter fields, feeding on turnips with patient resignation. Here, sheep stand, as if in a holding pen, on an elevated peninsula of land between the river and the flooded meadow.

160   PART III · THE LOWER COURSE OF THE RIVER

At no other time of the year are the woods so perfectly illuminated; cold days are the photographer's friend. The trees seem to stand together on their individual merits – we can count them, if we wish – and are not simply a congregation, as they seem in summer. Each species has its own timetable for shedding leaves; a different timetable in spring, when buds open, ash before oak and oak last of all.

Rosette leaves of winter-cress (*Barbarea vulgaris*); its stem leaves and yellow-petalled flowers will appear in April, but its rosette leaves are green all winter. A member of the cabbage family (Brassicaceae), and having the nutritional properties for which the family is known, the evergreen leaves were collected for salad during the vitamin-C-poor days of medieval winters.

The magic of winter is that rare events transform familiar landscapes – the geometry of wind-swept ice on the reeds of a water meadow, the rush and spread of the river in the vigour of high-water; a dazzle of snow on the footbridge over the River Swere in Barford St Michael adds a stroke of bright colour to a grey canvas. Trees feign death, herbaceous perennials follow suit, but winter-cress (*Barbarea vulgaris*) reverses the seasons and awaits winter for its blooming.

Birds change houses, swifts go to Africa, lapwings come to the Midlands. Lapwings were seen by the river at Barford St John in September 2003; also seen were small groups of long-tailed tits passing down the valley from South Newington to Wigginton in February, and bullfinches in hedges in March in the Meanders.

Top: Common hawthorn (*Crataegus monogyna*). Some birds feed on the red fruits as we do on olives –
they do not take great amounts all at once. As a result, the pretty fruits last longer and give colour to dull
days. Notice the green colouring of the lichens on the small branches.
Bottom: The village of South Newington in winter's robe.

The winter walker learns to look more closely at the characteristics by which trees tell us their names. The bud, even more than the leaf, is a better way to know them. When ash leaves have fallen, indelible black buds are prominently seen, a thumbprint of the species. Beech buds are long, slender and sharply pointed. A guide to trees in winter dress opens a new horizon of countryside pleasures.

When summer returns, the winter-wet grasslands will be flooded with the colours of meadow buttercup (*Ranunculus acris*), white flowering pignut (*Conopodium majus*), red clover (*Trifolium pratense*), salad burnet (*Sanguisorba minor* ssp. *minor*) and yellow-rattle (*Rhinanthus minor*). When hawthorn blossoms, and the river's edge draws pollinators from their winter quarters, we shall have forgotten its fruits, which give so much colour to winter's hedgerows.

Light streaming on to the bark of trees in Swere Bank Wood.

THE RIVER SWERE IN DEDDINGTON PARISH

T HE RIVER SWERE enters Deddington parish under cover of a shady wood, quietly and unseen from any place of public access. It forms the northern boundary of Deddington, from Deddington Mill to the River Cherwell. Greater spearwort (*Ranunculus lingua*), England's largest buttercup, grows in the shallow water of the mill pond on the grounds of a private residence. Leaving the mill pond, still water becomes animated and frothy, rushing down a sluice beside the mill house, and then again becoming the meandering Swere. The alternation of straight and sinuous reaches, of pool and riffle continues, as do other characteristics of the stream: its firm silt and clay banks on which grow grasses, herbs, crack-willow and hawthorn trees. Past Adderbury Bridge, the river is confined by a channel periodically dug out, made to obey the requirements of landowners who would limit flooding of low-lying fields.

With the first heavy autumn rains, the river rises quickly, perilously, ending the indolent dry days of August. On 14 October 2002 the river depth was 8 cm; after 38.3 mm of rainfall on 15th October, the depth the next day was 35 cm, 101 cm on 20th October, 138 cm on the 21st. The small floating plant, common duckweed (*Lemna minor*), which gathers in bays of the summer river, was swept away; branched bur-reed (*Sparganium erectum*), tall plant of summer's river edge, and coagulant of the shallow channel, was pressed beneath the rising tide of water.

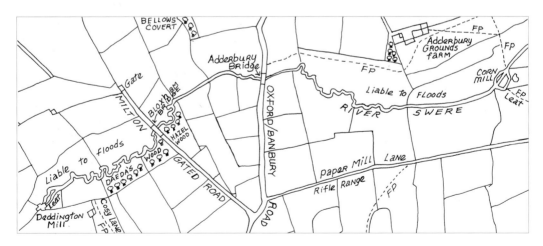

Above: Map of the River Swere in Deddington parish.

Right: The River Swere just east of Adderbury Bridge. The handsomely formed tree with dark green leaves on the Adderbury side of the river is an alder (*Alnus glutinosa*).

Near Adderbury Bridge

In this reach of the river, below and west of Adderbury Bridge, caddisfly larvae are plentiful beneath the gravelly stones, and branched bur-reed has crossed mid-stream, forcing summer's river to lace through its stems. The water below the bridge is yellow-green where the elliptical rosette-leaves of a dense colony of common water-starwort (*Callitriche stagnalis*) has congregated; common duckweed, with similar conglomerative tendencies, occurs above and below the bridge, idle in the slow stream. Perfoliate pondweed (*Potamogeton perfoliatus*) is growing in shallow (3-4 cm deep) rapidly-moving water east of the bridge, its only site in the river.

The green line of the course of the River Swere east of Adderbury Bridge, with crack-willows (*Salix fragilis*) on its left and a line of alders (*Alnus glutinosa*) in the background; red berries of common hawthorn (*Crataegus monogyna*) in the foreground of a ploughed field.

It is characteristic of the lower course of the river, almost anywhere from Adderbury Bridge to the Cherwell, that trees and shrubs are infrequent and are irregularly spaced on the high banks: one or two alders, an apple, ash and a few crack-willows give the appearance of parsimony more than richness. But the dog-rose (*Rosa canina*) that festoons common hawthorn (*Crataegus monogyna*) and bends toward the water, heavy in fruit, gives the pleasure of wildness. Herbaceous species seen in many places along the river include bittersweet (*Solanum dulcamara*), meadowsweet (*Filipendula ulmaria*), reed sweet-grass (*Glyceria maxima*), water figwort (*Scrophularia auriculata*) and water mint (*Mentha aquatica*).

The Old Paper Mill on Adderbury Grounds Farm

The Old Paper Mill was one of the three mills recorded for Deddington in 1087; called 'the Duchy mill' in 1583, it was 'leased to Nicholas Trippet, who built a new corn mill on the sites of one that had fallen into decay in the mid 16th century.'[47] In the late seventeenth century, the corn-mill was converted to a paper-mill, but by 1835 the paper-making equipment was sold as bankrupt stock. The damp brick wall below the mill is the site of an impressively large population of an attractive fern, maidenhair spleenwort (*Asplenium trichomanes*), with evergreen fronds and growing in neat rosettes.

The River Swere from Paper Mill Cottages

Just past the old mill there is a bridge over the river; from here the river passes between high unscalable banks, and measures between 4-6 cm deep in the shallows and 20 cm mid-stream in early summer. Young sycamore (*Acer pseudoplatanus*) trees reach out from both banks forming a canopy of shade. On the high banks where openings occur, reed canary-grass (*Phalaris arundinacea*) grows to 2 m high.

On a shallow muddy shore we found blue water-speedwell (*Veronica anagallis-aquatica*), water-cress (*Rorippa nasturtium-aquaticum*) and water forget-me-not (*Myosotis scorpioides*) – habitués of this habitat in every course of the river. In other sites of the river-margin vegetation, with water-logged mineral soils, there occurs fool's-water-cress (*Apium nodiflorum*), which is much more common in the upper course of the river – at Little Bridge Marsh, for example. Even in a small area, such as the length of the Swere, each species has a habitat, or variety of habitats, and a geographical distribution particular to it.

The River Edge on Castle Farm

Castle Farm is the last farm to border the Swere before it joins the River Cherwell; along its edge the river is mostly straight but in 1881, as the OS map of that date is witness, the Swere meandered and marsh plants grew on its sides. The work of deepening and straightening the channel, and draining the marsh, was carried out in the 1950s as part of a national effort to increase crop production.

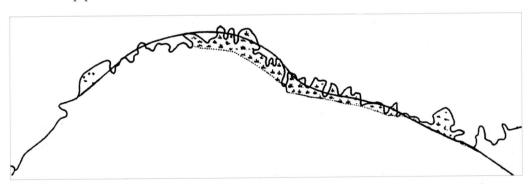

The nearly straight line of the Swere today superimposed on the meandering river of 1881. There are 29 marshes associated with the river but not one in Deddington, for here the adjoining fields are wide and gently sloping, and investment in land-drainage is more likely to be profitable.

The sparse and irregular spacing of trees that began above Adderbury Bridge continues to the Cherwell: a few alders, hawthorns, a good-sized oak and three oak saplings. Grey willow (*Salix cinerea*) is more common than crack-willow; of special interest, because of its size, is the buckthorn (*Rhamnus cathartica*) tree on the edge of Bourne Field, handsomely proportioned and laden with fruits.

Buckthorn (*Rhamnus cathartica*) is not common in the wooded edges of the Swere, except along the Wigginton road, where there are ten tall buckthorn trees on the river bank. The photograph shows the four petals of each flower which hang on short pedicels and arise in bunches from the axil of the leaves.

Journey's End

As it did east of Little Barford Mill, reed sweet-grass, tall and graceful, grows densely, sometimes in the channel, close to mid-stream; but then moving towards the confluence of the two rivers, its abundance diminishes, and branched bur-reed appears. Just as quickly there is another change, a signal that the Swere is only moments away from joining the larger tributary of the Thames: dense clumps of tall dark stems of common club-rush (*Schoenoplectus lacustris*). Common club-rush is widespread in the Cherwell, conceals moorhen and suggests the hiding place of baby Moses.

Joining the River Cherwell without foam or foment, the Swere sheds the water it has collected from springs, streams and run-off over a distance of 25.3 km. The precise location of the confluence is obscured by common reed (*Phragmites australis*), which may grow to 3.5 m tall, perhaps the world's commonest giant grass. As soon as the Swere enters the broad-shouldered and fast-moving Cherwell, it is lost in the hurry of a larger world, and our story ends. When we first showed photographs of the river, at an exhibition in Wales, a man from Devon studied them carefully: 'We could do that!' he said. And that is our hope, that the pleasure we have had in tracing the course of a small neighbourhood river will be repeated in other parts of the British Isles.

Common reed (*Phragmites australis*) where the Swere meets the Cherwell.

		1	2	3	4	5	6	7	8	9	10	11	12	13	14	15
Alismataceae	Alisma plantago-aquatica	–	–	✓	–	–	✓	–	–	–	–	–	–	–	–	–
	Sagittaria sagittifolia	–	–	–	–	–	–	–	–	–	–	–	–	–	–	–
Apiaceae	Angelica sylvestris	–	–	✓	✓	✓	✓	✓	✓	✓	–	–	✓	✓	✓	✓
	Apium nodiflorum	✓	✓	✓	✓	✓	–	✓	✓	–	✓	–	–	–	–	–
	Berula erecta	–	–	–	–	–	–	–	–	–	–	–	✓	✓	–	–
Asteraceae	Achillaea ptarmica	–	–	–	–	✓	–	–	–	–	–	–	–	–	–	–
	Cirsium palustre	–	–	✓	✓	✓	–	–	–	✓	✓	✓	✓	✓	✓	✓
	Eupatorium cannabinum	✓	✓	✓	–	✓	–	–	✓	–	✓	–	–	–	✓	✓
	Gnaphalium uliginosum	–	–	–	–	–	–	–	–	–	–	–	–	–	–	–
	Petasites hybridus	–	–	–	–	–	–	–	–	–	–	–	–	–	–	–
	Pulicaria dysenterica	–	–	✓	–	✓	–	✓	–	–	–	–	✓	✓	–	–
Boraginaceae	Myosotis discolor	–	–	–	–	–	–	–	–	–	–	–	–	–	–	–
	Myosotis scorpioides	–	–	✓	✓	✓	–	–	✓	–	✓	–	✓	✓	✓	✓
	Symphytum officinale	–	–	–	–	–	–	–	–	–	–	–	–	–	–	–
Brassicaceae	Barbarea vulgaris	–	–	–	–	–	–	–	✓	–	–	–	–	–	–	–
	Cardamine flexuosa	–	–	✓	–	–	–	–	✓	–	✓	–	✓	–	–	–
	Cardamine pratensis	–	–	✓	–	✓	–	✓	✓	✓	✓	–	–	–	–	–
	Rorippa nasturtium-aquaticum	–	–	✓	–	✓	–	–	✓	✓	✓	–	–	–	–	–
Callitrichaceae	Callitriche stagnalis	–	–	✓	–	–	–	–	–	–	–	–	–	–	–	–
Caryophyllaceae	Lychnis flos-cuculi	–	–	✓	–	✓	–	–	–	–	✓	✓	–	✓	–	✓
	Myosoton aquaticum	–	–	–	–	–	–	–	–	–	–	–	–	–	–	–
	Stellaria graminea	–	–	–	–	✓	–	–	–	–	–	–	–	✓	✓	–
	Stellaria uliginosa	–	–	✓	–	–	–	–	–	–	✓	–	–	–	–	–
Clusiaceae	Hypericum maculatum	–	–	–	–	–	–	–	✓	–	–	–	–	–	–	–
	Hypericum tetrapterum	–	–	✓	–	–	–	✓	✓	–	✓	–	–	–	–	–
Cyperaceae	Carex acuta	–	–	–	–	–	–	–	–	–	–	–	–	–	–	–
	Carex acutiformis	–	–	✓	✓	–	–	–	✓	✓	–	–	–	✓	d	–
	Carex disticha	–	–	–	–	–	–	–	–	–	–	–	–	–	–	–
	Carex hirta	–	–	✓	–	✓	–	–	–	–	–	–	✓	✓	–	✓
	Carex otrubae	–	–	✓	–	–	–	–	–	–	–	–	–	✓	–	–
	Carex ovalis	–	–	–	–	–	–	–	–	–	–	–	–	–	–	–
	Carex panicea	–	–	–	–	–	–	–	–	–	–	–	–	–	–	–
	Carex paniculata	–	–	✓	–	–	–	–	–	–	–	–	–	–	–	–
	Carex pendula	–	–	–	–	–	–	–	–	–	–	–	–	–	–	–
	Carex remota	–	–	–	–	–	–	–	–	–	–	–	–	–	–	–
	Carex riparia	–	–	✓	–	–	–	–	–	–	d	–	–	✓	–	✓
	Carex spicata	–	–	–	–	–	–	–	–	–	–	–	–	–	–	–
	Carex viridula ssp. brachyrrhyncha	–	–	–	–	–	–	✓	–	–	–	–	–	–	–	–
	Eleocharis palustris	–	–	✓	–	–	–	–	✓	–	✓	–	–	–	–	–
	Isolepis setacea	–	–	–	–	–	–	–	–	–	✓	–	–	–	–	–
	Schoenoplectus lacustris	–	✓	–	–	–	✓	–	✓	–	–	–	–	–	–	–
	Scirpus sylvaticus	–	–	✓	–	–	–	–	–	–	–	–	–	✓	–	–
Dipsacaceae	Dipsacus fullonum	–	–	–	–	–	–	–	–	–	–	–	–	–	–	–
Equisetaceae	Equisetum palustre	–	–	✓	–	–	–	–	–	–	✓	–	✓	–	–	✓
	Equisetum telmateia	–	–	–	–	–	–	–	–	–	✓	✓	–	–	–	–
Fabaceae	Lathyrus pratensis	–	–	✓	–	✓	–	✓	✓	✓	–	–	✓	✓	✓	✓
	Lotus pedunculatus	–	–	–	–	–	✓	✓	–	✓	–	–	–	–	–	✓
Haloragaceae	Myriophyllum spicatum	–	–	–	–	–	–	–	–	–	–	–	–	–	–	–
Hippuridaceae	Hippuris vulgaris	–	✓	–	–	–	–	–	–	–	–	–	–	–	–	–
Hydrocharitaceae	Elodea canadensis	–	–	✓	–	–	✓	–	–	–	–	–	–	–	–	–
	Lagarosiphon major	–	–	✓	–	–	–	–	–	–	–	–	–	✓	–	–
	Stratiotes aloides	–	–	–	–	–	–	–	–	–	–	–	–	✓	–	–
Iridaceae	Iris pseudacorus	–	–	✓	✓	–	✓	–	✓	–	–	–	–	✓	–	–

Key: d = dominant

River Swere Marsh Sites

1 Tufa Ponds in Kiteney Copse
2 Mare's-tail Pond and Marsh
3 Horsetail and Priory Mill Ponds
4 Bulrush Marshes

5 Juncus Marshes
6 Heron Pond
7 Swere Bank Marsh
8 Clearwater Pond
9 Floodplain Wood Marsh
10 Church Marsh

11 Swerford marshes below motte and bailey
12 Little Bridge Marsh
13 Island Marsh and Pond
14 Carex Marsh
15 Mint Marsh

16	17	18	19	20	21	22	23	24	25	26	27	28	29	30
–	✓	–	–	✓	✓	–	–	–	–	✓	–	–	✓	
–	–	–	–	–	–	–	–	–	–	–	–	–	–	Bloxham Bridge area
–	–	✓	–	✓	✓	✓	✓	–	–	✓	–	✓	✓	
✓	✓	–	–	✓	–	–	–	✓	✓	✓	–	✓	✓	Scattered throughout
–	–	–	–	–	–	–	–	–	–	–	–	–	–	Occasional by river edge
–	–	–	–	–	–	–	–	–	–	–	–	–	–	
✓	✓	✓	✓	✓	✓	–	✓	✓	–	✓	✓	✓	✓	
✓	✓	–	–	✓	–	–	–	–	–	✓	–	✓	–	Rare on lower course
–	–	–	–	✓	✓	–	–	–	–	–	–	–	–	
–	–	✓	–	–	✓	✓	–	–	–	–	–	✓	✓	More common on northern. tributary
✓	–	–	–	–	–	–	✓	–	–	–	–	–	✓	
–	✓	–	–	–	–	–	–	✓	–	–	–	–	–	
✓	✓	–	–	–	–	–	✓	✓	–	✓	–	✓	–	Scattered throughout
–	–	–	–	–	–	–	–	✓	–	–	–	–	–	Rare on lower course
–	–	✓	✓	✓	✓	–	–	–	✓	–	–	✓	✓	Frequent in middle and lower courses
–	✓	✓	–	✓	–	–	–	–	–	–	✓	✓	✓	Scattered in middle and lower courses
✓	✓	✓	✓	✓	✓	–	✓	–	✓	–	✓	✓	✓	
–	✓	–	✓	✓	–	–	–	–	✓	–	–	–	–	Occasional in lower course
–	–	–	–	–	–	–	–	–	–	–	–	–	–	Occasional in lower course
✓	✓	✓	✓	✓	✓	–	✓	✓	–	✓	✓	✓	✓	
✓	–	–	–	–	–	–	–	–	–	–	–	–	–	Scattered in lower course
–	–	✓	✓	✓	✓	–	✓	✓	–	–	–	✓	✓	
–	✓	–	–	✓	–	–	–	✓	–	–	–	–	✓	
–	–	–	–	✓	✓	–	–	✓	–	–	–	–	–	
✓	–	–	–	✓	–	✓	–	✓	–	✓	–	✓	✓	Rare in lower course
–	✓	–	–	–	d	–	–	–	–	–	–	–	–	
–	✓	–	d	–	–	–	✓	✓	–	–	–	–	d	
–	–	–	–	–	✓	–	–	–	–	–	–	–	✓	
✓	✓	–	✓	–	✓	–	✓	✓	–	✓	–	✓		
✓	–	–	–	–	–	–	✓	✓	✓	–	–	–	–	
–	✓	–	–	–	–	–	–	–	–	✓	–	–	–	
–	–	✓	✓	–	✓	–	–	–	–	–	–	–	–	
–	✓	–	–	–	–	–	–	–	–	–	–	–	–	
–	–	–	–	–	–	–	–	–	–	✓	✓	–		Only in northern tributary and planted in Swerford village pond
–	–	–	–	–	–	–	–	–	–	–	✓	–		
d	–	✓	–	–	d	–	–	–	–	–	–	–	–	
–	–	–	–	–	–	–	✓	–	–	–	–	–	–	
–	–	–	–	–	–	–	–	–	–	–	–	–	–	
✓	–	✓	✓	–	–	✓	–	✓	–	–	–	–	–	
–	✓	–	–	–	–	–	–	–	–	–	–	–	–	
–	–	–	–	–	–	–	–	–	–	–	–	–	–	Occasional in lower course
–	–	–	–	✓	✓	–	–	–	–	–	–	–	✓	
–	–	✓	–	✓	–	–	–	✓	–	–	–	–	–	Occasional in lower and middle course
–	✓	✓	–	✓	✓	–	✓	✓	–	✓	–	✓		
–	–	–	–	–	–	–	✓	–	–	–	–	–	In the Swerford area	
✓	–	✓	–	–	✓	✓	✓	–	–	–	✓	–	✓	
✓	✓	✓	–	–	–	✓	✓	✓	–	–	–	✓		
–	–	–	✓	–	–	–	–	–	–	–	–	–	–	In Pony Meadow Pond. Introduced?
–	–	–	–	–	–	–	–	–	–	–	–	–	–	
–	–	–	–	✓	–	–	–	–	–	–	–	–	–	
–	–	–	✓	✓	–	–	–	–	–	–	–	–	–	Introduced
–	–	–	–	–	–	–	–	–	–	–	–	–	–	Introduced
–	✓	✓	–	✓	✓	–	–	✓	–	✓	–	–	✓	

16 Quarry Spring Marsh
17 Ribbon Marsh
18 Wigginton Meanders Marsh
19 Peat Marsh
20 Horse-Pasture Pond and Marsh
21 Long Marsh and Pond

22 Walkway Marsh
23 Oak Field Marshes
24 Marsh and ditches opposite The Dingle
25 Barford Fish Ponds
26 The Scrapes

Northern Tributary

27 Marigold Marsh
28 Moors Marsh
29 Cradle Farm Marsh
30 Water Plants and River Edge Species

	1	2	3	4	5	6	7	8	9	10	11	12	13	14	15
Juncaceae Juncus acutiflorus	–	–	–	–	✓	–	✓	✓	–	–	–	–	✓	–	–
Juncus articulatus	–	–	–	–	–	–	✓	–	–	✓	–	✓	✓	–	✓
Juncus bufonius	–	–	✓	–	–	–	–	–	–	–	–	–	–	–	–
Juncus conglomeratus	–	–	–	–	–	–	–	✓	–	–	–	✓	✓	–	–
Juncus effusus	–	–	✓	✓	✓	–	–	✓	✓	–	–	✓	✓	–	✓
Juncus inflexus	–	–	✓	–	d	✓	✓	✓	✓	✓	✓	✓	–	✓	✓
Juncus subnodulosus	–	–	–	–	✓	–	–	–	–	–	–	–	–	–	✓
Juncaginaceae Triglochin palustre	–	–	–	–	–	–	✓	–	–	–	–	–	–	–	–
Lamiaceae Ajuga reptans	–	–	✓	–	✓	–	–	–	✓	✓	–	✓	–	–	–
Galeopsis tetrahit	–	–	–	–	–	–	–	–	–	–	–	–	–	–	–
Lycopus europaeus	–	–	–	–	–	–	–	–	–	–	–	–	–	–	–
Mentha aquatica	✓	✓	✓	–	✓	✓	✓	✓	✓	✓	–	✓	–	–	d
Scutellaria galericulata	–	–	–	–	–	–	–	–	–	–	–	–	–	–	–
Stachys x ambigua	–	–	–	–	–	–	–	–	–	–	–	–	–	–	–
Stachys palustris	–	–	–	–	–	–	–	–	–	–	–	–	–	–	–
Lemnaceae Lemna minor	–	–	–	–	–	–	–	–	–	–	–	–	–	–	–
Lythraceae Lythrum salicaria	–	–	–	–	–	–	–	–	–	–	–	✓	✓	–	–
Menyanthaceae Menyanthes trifoliata	–	–	–	–	–	–	–	–	–	–	–	–	–	–	–
Nymphoides peltata	–	–	–	–	–	–	–	–	–	–	–	–	✓	–	–
Nymphaceae Nuphar lutea	–	–	–	–	–	–	–	–	–	–	–	–	–	–	–
Nymphaea alba	–	–	✓	–	–	✓	–	–	–	–	–	–	–	–	–
Onagraceae Chamerion angustifolium	–	–	✓	–	–	–	–	✓	–	–	–	–	–	–	–
Epilobium hirsutum	–	–	✓	✓	✓	–	✓	✓	✓	✓	–	✓	✓	✓	✓
Epilobium parviflorum	–	–	–	–	✓	–	✓	✓	✓	✓	–	✓	✓	–	✓
Orchidaceae Dactylorhiza fuchsii	✓	–	–	–	–	–	–	✓	–	–	✓	–	–	–	–
Dactylorhiza praetermissa	–	–	–	–	–	–	–	–	–	–	–	–	–	–	–
Poaceae Alopecurus geniculatus	–	–	–	–	–	–	–	–	–	–	–	–	–	–	–
Catabrosa aquatica	–	–	–	–	–	–	–	–	–	–	–	–	–	–	–
Deschampsia cespitosa	✓	–	✓	–	✓	✓	✓	✓	✓	–	✓	✓	✓	✓	–
Glyceria fluitans	–	–	–	–	–	–	–	✓	–	–	–	–	–	–	✓
Glyceria maxima	–	–	✓	–	–	–	–	–	–	–	✓	✓	–	–	–
Phalaris arundinacea	✓	–	✓	✓	✓	✓	–	✓	–	–	✓	✓	✓	–	✓
Phragmites australis	–	–	✓	–	–	✓	–	✓	–	–	–	✓	✓	–	–
Polygonaceae Persicaria amphibia	–	–	–	–	–	–	–	–	–	–	–	–	–	–	–
Persicaria bistorta	–	–	✓	–	–	–	–	–	–	–	–	–	–	–	–
Persicaria hydropiper	–	–	–	–	–	–	–	–	–	–	–	–	–	–	–
Rumex lapathifolia	–	–	–	–	–	–	–	–	–	–	–	–	–	–	–
Rumex sanguineus	–	–	✓	✓	✓	✓	–	–	✓	✓	✓	✓	✓	✓	✓
Potamogetonaceae Potamogeton natans	–	✓	✓	–	–	–	–	–	–	–	–	–	–	–	–
Primulaceae Lysimachia nummularia	–	–	–	–	–	–	–	–	–	–	–	–	✓	–	–
Lysimachia vulgaris	–	–	–	–	–	–	–	–	–	–	–	–	✓	–	–
Ranunculaceae Caltha palustris	–	–	✓	–	–	–	–	–	✓	✓	✓	✓	✓	–	–
Ranunculus ficaria	–	–	✓	–	✓	–	–	✓	✓	✓	–	✓	–	–	–
Ranunculus peltatus	–	–	–	–	–	–	–	–	–	–	–	–	–	–	–
Ranunculus repens	–	–	✓	–	✓	–	–	✓	✓	✓	–	✓	✓	✓	–
Ranunculus sceleratus	–	–	–	–	–	–	–	–	–	–	–	–	–	–	–
Ranunculus trichophyllus	–	–	–	–	–	–	–	–	–	–	–	–	–	–	–
Rosaceae Filipendula ulmaria	–	✓	✓	✓	d	✓	✓	✓	✓	✓	–	✓	✓	–	✓
Rubiaceae Galium palustre	–	–	✓	–	✓	–	✓	–	✓	✓	✓	✓	✓	–	✓
Scrophulariaceae Scrophularia auriculata	–	–	✓	–	✓	–	–	✓	✓	✓	–	✓	–	–	–
Veronica anagallis-aquatica	–	–	–	–	✓	–	–	–	–	–	–	–	–	✓	–
Veronica beccabunga	–	–	✓	–	✓	–	–	✓	✓	✓	–	✓	–	–	–
Sparganiaceae Sparganium erectum	–	–	✓	–	–	✓	–	✓	–	–	✓	✓	✓	–	d
Typhaceae Typha angustifolia	–	–	–	–	–	–	–	✓	–	–	–	–	–	–	–
Typha latifolia	–	✓	✓	d	✓	–	–	–	–	–	–	✓	–	–	–
Valerianaceae Valeriana officinalis	–	–	–	–	–	–	–	–	–	–	–	–	–	–	–

Key: d = dominant

River Swere Marsh Sites

1 Tufa Ponds in Kiteney Copse
2 Mare's-tail Pond and Marsh
3 Horsetail and Priory Mill Ponds
4 Bulrush Marshes
5 Juncus Marshes
6 Heron Pond
7 Swere Bank Marsh
8 Clearwater Pond
9 Floodplain Wood Marsh
10 Church Marsh
11 Swerford marshes below motte and bailey
12 Little Bridge Marsh
13 Island Marsh and Pond
14 Carex Marsh
15 Mint Marsh

16	17	18	19	20	21	22	23	24	25	26	27	28	29	30
d	–	✓	–	–	✓	–	–	–	–	–	–	–	–	
✓	✓	–	✓	✓	–	–	✓	✓	–	✓	✓	–	–	
–	✓	–	✓	✓	✓	–	✓	–	✓	–	–	–	–	
–	–	–	–	–	✓	–	✓	–	–	–	✓	–	–	
✓	✓	–	✓	–	✓	–	✓	✓	–	✓	✓	✓	✓	
✓	✓	d	✓	✓	✓	–	✓	✓	–	✓	✓	✓	✓	
–	–	✓	–	–	–	–	–	–	–	–	–	–	–	
–	–	–	✓	–	–	–	–	–	–	–	–	–	–	
–	✓	✓	✓	✓	–	–	–	✓	✓	–	–	✓	✓	
–	–	–	–	✓	–	–	✓	✓	–	–	–	–	–	Occasional in middle and lower courses
–	–	–	✓	–	–	–	–	–	✓	–	–	–	–	Scattered in lower course
✓	–	–	✓	✓	✓	✓	✓	✓	✓	✓	✓	✓	✓	Frequent in middle and lower courses
✓	✓	–	–	✓	✓	–	✓	–	–	–	–	–	–	Occasional in lower course
–	–	–	–	–	–	✓	–	–	–	–	–	–	–	Rare in S. Newington area
–	–	–	–	–	–	✓	–	–	–	–	–	–	–	Rare in S. Newington area
–	–	–	–	✓	✓	–	–	–	–	–	–	–	–	Occasional in lower course
–	✓	✓	–	✓	✓	✓	✓	✓	–	✓	✓	✓	✓	Frequent in middle and lower courses
–	–	–	–	–	–	–	–	–	–	–	–	–	–	Pond at East End, Swerford. Introduced
–	–	–	–	–	–	–	–	–	–	–	–	–	–	Introduced
–	–	–	–	–	✓	–	–	–	–	–	–	–	–	Occasional in lower sections
–	–	–	–	✓	–	–	–	–	–	–	–	–	–	Introduced
–	–	–	–	–	–	✓	–	✓	–	–	–	–	–	
✓	–	✓	–	✓	✓	✓	✓	✓	✓	✓	✓	✓	✓	
–	✓	–	✓	✓	–	–	✓	–	–	✓	✓	✓		
–	–	–	–	–	–	–	✓	–	–	–	–	–	–	
–	–	–	–	–	–	–	–	–	–	–	✓	✓		
–	✓	✓	✓	–	–	–	–	–	–	–	–	–	✓	
–	–	–	–	✓	–	–	–	–	–	–	–	–	–	
✓	✓	✓	–	–	✓	–	✓	✓	–	d	–	✓	–	
d	✓	✓	✓	–	✓	–	–	✓	–	✓	✓	–	✓	
✓	✓	✓	–	–	–	✓	–	–	✓	✓	–	–	–	Frequent in lower course
✓	✓	✓	–	✓	d	✓	✓	✓	–	d	–	✓	✓	
–	–	–	–	–	–	–	–	–	–	–	–	–	–	Frequent near to Swere/Cherwell confluence
–	–	–	–	–	✓	–	–	✓	✓	–	–	–	–	Rare in lower course
–	–	–	–	–	✓	–	✓	–	–	–	–	–	–	
–	–	–	–	✓	✓	–	–	–	–	–	–	–	–	
–	–	–	–	–	–	–	–	–	–	–	–	–	–	River by Horse-Pasture Pond
✓	–	✓	–	✓	–	–	✓	–	–	–	–	–	–	
–	–	✓	✓	–	–	–	–	–	–	–	–	–	–	
✓	–	✓	–	–	✓	–	✓	–	–	–	–	–	✓	
–	–	–	–	–	–	–	–	–	–	–	–	–	–	Introduced?
✓	✓	✓	✓	✓	✓	–	–	–	–	–	✓	✓	✓	
✓	✓	✓	✓	✓	✓	–	✓	✓	–	✓	✓	–		
–	–	–	–	–	✓	–	–	–	–	–	–	–	–	Pony Meadow Pond. Introduced?
–	✓	✓	✓	✓	✓	–	✓	✓	–	✓	✓	✓		
–	–	–	–	–	–	–	✓	✓	–	–	–	–	–	By river in lower course – occasional
–	–	–	–	✓	–	–	–	–	–	–	–	–	–	Pony Meadow Pond. Introduced?
✓	✓	d	d	✓	d	✓	✓	✓	–	✓	–	✓	✓	Common throughout
–	✓	–	–	✓	–	–	✓	✓	–	✓	✓	✓		
✓	✓	✓	✓	✓	✓	✓	✓	✓	✓	✓	✓	–	✓	Common throughout
✓	–	✓	–	✓	–	–	–	–	✓	✓	–	–	–	Occasional in middle and lower courses
✓	✓	✓	✓	✓	–	–	–	✓	✓	✓	✓	✓	✓	
d	✓	–	–	✓	d	✓	✓	✓	–	–	–	–	–	Frequent in middle and lower courses
–	–	–	–	–	✓	–	–	–	–	–	–	–	–	
–	–	–	✓	–	–	–	–	–	–	d	–	✓	✓	
–	–	–	–	–	–	✓	✓	–	–	–	–	–	–	Rare in middle and lower courses

16 Quarry Spring Marsh
17 Ribbon Marsh
18 Wigginton Meanders Marsh
19 Peat Marsh
20 Horse-Pasture Pond and Marsh
21 Long Marsh and Pond

22 Walkway Marsh
23 Oak Field Marshes
24 Marsh and ditches opposite The Dingle
25 Barford Fish Ponds
26 The Scrapes

Northern Tributary

27 Marigold Marsh
28 Moors Marsh
29 Cradle Farm Marsh
30 Water Plants and River Edge Species

		A	B	C	D	E	F	G	H	I	J	K	L	M	N	O	P
Apiaceae	Conopodium majus	–	✓	✓	✓	✓	✓	✓	✓	✓	–	✓	✓	–	✓	✓	✓
	Heracleum sphondylium	–	–	–	–	–	–	–	–	✓	✓	–	–	–	–	–	–
	Pimpinella saxifraga	✓	–	–	✓	–	✓	✓	✓	✓	–	–	–	✓	✓	–	–
Asteraceae	Achillaea millefolium	✓	✓	–	✓	–	–	–	✓	✓	✓	✓	✓	✓	✓	✓	–
	Bellis perennis	✓	✓	–	–	–	–	–	–	✓	✓	–	✓	✓	✓	–	✓
	Carduus crispus	–	–	✓	✓	–	✓	✓	–	✓	✓	–	–	✓	✓	–	–
	Carduus nutans	✓	–	–	–	–	–	–	–	✓	✓	–	–	–	✓	–	–
	Centaurea nigra	✓	✓	✓	✓	✓	✓	✓	✓	✓	✓	–	✓	✓	✓	✓	✓
	Centaurea scabiosa	✓	–	–	–	–	–	–	–	–	–	–	✓	–	–	–	–
	Cirsium acaule	✓	–	–	✓	–	–	–	–	–	–	–	✓	–	✓	–	–
	Cirsium arvense	✓	✓	✓	✓	✓	✓	–	✓	✓	✓	✓	✓	✓	✓	✓	✓
	Cirsium eriophorum	✓	–	–	–	–	–	–	–	✓	✓	–	–	–	–	–	–
	Cirsium palustre	–	–	–	–	–	–	✓	✓	✓	–	✓	✓	✓	✓	✓	✓
	Cirsium vulgare	✓	✓	–	–	–	–	✓	✓	✓	✓	–	–	✓	–	–	–
	Crepis capillaris	–	–	✓	✓	–	–	–	–	–	–	–	–	–	–	✓	✓
	Hypochaeris radicata	✓	✓	–	✓	✓	–	✓	–	✓	✓	✓	✓	✓	✓	✓	✓
	Leontodon autumnalis	✓	–	–	✓	✓	–	–	–	✓	✓	–	–	–	✓	–	–
	Leontodon hispidus	✓	–	✓	✓	✓	–	✓	✓	✓	–	✓	✓	✓	✓	✓	–
	Leucanthemum vulgare	✓	–	–	–	–	✓	–	✓	–	✓	–	✓	–	✓	–	–
	Picris hieracioides	✓	–	–	–	–	–	–	–	–	–	–	✓	–	–	–	–
	Pilosella officinarum	✓	–	–	✓	–	–	–	–	✓	✓	–	✓	–	–	–	–
	Senecio jacobaea	✓	–	–	–	–	–	–	–	✓	✓	✓	✓	✓	✓	✓	–
	Serratula tinctoria	–	–	–	–	–	–	–	–	–	–	–	–	–	–	–	–
	Sonchus arvensis	–	–	–	–	–	–	–	–	–	✓	–	–	–	–	–	–
	Taraxacum officinale	✓	✓	✓	–	✓	✓	–	✓	✓	✓	✓	✓	✓	✓	✓	✓
	Tragopogon pratensis	✓	–	–	–	–	✓	–	–	–	–	–	–	–	–	–	–
Boraginaceae	Myosotis arvensis	✓	–	–	–	–	–	–	–	✓	✓	–	–	–	✓	✓	–
Brassicaceae	Cardamine pratensis	–	✓	–	–	✓	–	✓	–	✓	–	–	–	✓	✓	✓	✓
Campanulaceae	Campanula glomerata	✓	–	–	–	–	–	–	–	–	–	–	–	–	–	–	–
	Campanula rotundifolia	✓	–	–	–	–	–	–	–	✓	✓	–	✓	✓	✓	✓	✓
Caryophyllaceae	Arenaria serpyllifolia	–	–	–	–	–	–	–	–	✓	–	–	–	–	✓	–	–
	Cerastium fontanum	✓	✓	✓	✓	✓	✓	✓	✓	✓	–	✓	✓	✓	✓	✓	✓
	Cerastium glomeratum	–	–	–	–	–	–	✓	✓	✓	–	–	–	✓	✓	–	–
	Cerastium semidecandrum	–	–	–	–	–	–	–	–	✓	–	–	–	–	✓	–	–
	Silene alba	–	–	–	–	–	–	✓	✓	✓	–	–	–	–	–	–	–
	Silene vulgaris	✓	–	–	–	–	–	–	–	✓	–	–	–	–	–	–	–
	Stellaria graminea	–	–	–	✓	–	–	✓	✓	✓	–	–	–	–	✓	✓	✓
Cistaceae	Helianthemum nummularium	✓	–	–	–	–	–	–	–	✓	–	–	✓	–	–	–	–
Clusiaceae	Hypericum perforatum	✓	–	–	–	–	–	–	✓	✓	✓	–	✓	✓	–	–	–
Cyperaceae	Carex flacca	✓	–	–	–	–	–	–	–	–	✓	–	✓	–	–	✓	✓
	Carex hirta	–	–	–	–	✓	✓	✓	✓	–	✓	–	–	–	–	–	–
	Carex muricata	–	–	–	–	–	–	–	–	✓	–	–	–	–	–	–	–
	Carex panicea	–	–	–	–	–	✓	✓	–	–	–	–	–	–	–	–	–
Dipsaceae	Knautia arvensis	✓	–	–	–	–	–	–	–	✓	–	–	–	–	–	–	–
	Scabiosa columbaria	✓	–	–	–	–	–	–	–	–	–	–	–	✓	✓	–	–
	Succisa pratensis	✓	–	–	–	✓	–	–	✓	✓	–	–	✓	✓	–	✓	✓
Equisetaceae	Equisetum arvense	–	–	–	✓	✓	–	–	✓	✓	✓	–	–	–	–	✓	✓
Fabaceae	Anthyllis vulneraria	✓	–	–	–	–	–	–	–	✓	✓	–	–	–	–	–	–
	Hippocrepis comosa	✓	–	–	–	–	–	–	–	–	–	–	–	–	–	–	–
	Lathyrus linifolius	–	–	–	–	–	–	–	–	–	–	–	✓	✓	–	–	–
	Lathyrus pratensis	✓	–	✓	✓	✓	–	✓	✓	✓	✓	–	–	–	✓	✓	✓
	Lotus corniculatus	✓	✓	✓	✓	✓	✓	✓	✓	✓	✓	✓	✓	✓	✓	✓	✓
	Medicago lupulina	–	–	–	✓	–	–	–	✓	✓	✓	–	–	–	–	–	–
	Onobrychis viciifolia	✓	–	–	–	–	–	–	–	–	–	–	–	–	–	–	–
	Ononis repens	✓	–	–	–	–	–	–	–	–	–	–	–	–	–	–	–
	Trifolium campestre	–	–	–	–	–	–	–	✓	–	✓	–	–	–	–	✓	–
	Trifolium hybridum	–	–	–	–	–	–	–	–	–	✓	–	–	–	–	–	–
	Trifolium pratense	✓	✓	✓	✓	✓	✓	✓	✓	✓	✓	✓	✓	✓	✓	✓	✓
	Trifolium repens	✓	✓	✓	✓	✓	✓	✓	✓	✓	✓	✓	✓	✓	✓	✓	✓
	Ulex europaeus	–	–	–	–	–	–	–	–	–	–	–	✓	–	–	✓	–
	Vicia cracca	✓	–	–	–	–	–	–	–	✓	–	–	–	–	–	–	✓
	Vicia hirsuta	✓	–	–	–	–	–	–	–	–	✓	–	–	✓	✓	–	–
	Vicia sepium	–	–	–	✓	–	–	–	–	–	✓	–	–	–	–	–	–
Gentianaceae	Centaurium erythraea	✓	–	–	–	–	–	–	–	✓	✓	–	–	✓	✓	–	–
	Gentianella amarella	✓	–	–	–	–	–	–	–	–	–	–	–	–	–	–	–
Geraniaceae	Erodium cicutarium	–	–	–	–	–	–	–	–	✓	–	–	–	✓	✓	–	–
	Geranium dissectum	–	–	–	–	✓	–	✓	✓	✓	✓	–	–	–	–	✓	–
	Geranium molle	–	–	–	–	–	–	–	–	✓	–	–	✓	✓	✓	✓	–
	Geranium pratense	–	–	–	–	–	✓	–	✓	✓	–	✓	–	✓	–	✓	–
Juncaceae	Luzula campestris	–	✓	✓	✓	✓	✓	✓	✓	✓	–	✓	✓	✓	✓	✓	✓
Lamiaceae	Ajuga reptans	–	✓	✓	–	–	–	–	–	–	✓	–	✓	–	–	✓	✓
	Glechoma hederacea	–	✓	–	–	–	✓	✓	✓	✓	–	–	–	✓	–	✓	✓
	Mentha arvensis	–	–	–	–	–	–	–	–	✓	–	–	–	–	–	–	–

		A	B	C	D	E	F	G	H	I	J	K	L	M	N	O	P
	Prunella vulgaris	✓	✓	–	✓	✓	✓	✓	✓	✓	✓	–	✓	✓	✓	✓	✓
	Stachys officinalis	–	–	✓	–	✓	–	–	✓	–	–	–	✓	–	✓	✓	✓
	Thymus polytrichus	✓	–	–	–	–	–	–	–	–	–	–	–	–	–	–	–
Liliaceae	Hyacinthoides non-scripta	–	✓	–	–	–	–	–	✓	–	–	–	–	–	–	–	–
Linaceae	Linum catharticum	✓	–	–	–	–	–	–	–	–	–	–	–	–	–	–	–
Malvaceae	Malva moschata	–	–	–	–	–	–	✓	–	–	–	–	–	–	–	–	–
Ophioglossaceae	Ophioglossum vulgatum	–	✓	–	–	–	–	–	–	–	–	–	✓	–	–	–	–
Orchidaceae	Dactylorhiza fuchsii	✓	–	–	–	✓	–	✓	–	–	–	–	–	–	–	–	✓
	Dactylorhiza maculata ssp. ericetorum	–	–	–	–	–	–	–	–	–	–	–	–	–	✓	✓	✓
	Ophrys apifera	✓	–	–	–	–	–	–	–	–	–	–	–	–	–	–	–
Plantaginaceae	Plantago lanceolata	✓	✓	✓	✓	✓	✓	✓	✓	✓	✓	✓	✓	✓	✓	✓	✓
	Plantago major	✓	✓	–	–	–	–	–	–	–	–	✓	✓	–	–	–	–
	Plantago media	✓	–	–	–	–	–	–	✓	✓	–	–	✓	✓	✓	–	–
Poaceae	Agrostis canina	–	–	–	–	–	✓	✓	–	–	–	–	–	–	–	–	–
	Agrostis stolonifera	–	✓	✓	✓	✓	✓	✓	✓	✓	✓	✓	✓	✓	✓	✓	✓
	Alopecurus pratensis	✓	✓	✓	✓	✓	✓	✓	✓	✓	✓	✓	✓	✓	✓	✓	✓
	Anthoxanthum odoratum	✓	✓	✓	✓	✓	✓	✓	✓	✓	✓	–	✓	✓	✓	✓	✓
	Arrhenatherum elatius	–	✓	✓	✓	✓	✓	✓	✓	✓	✓	✓	✓	✓	✓	✓	✓
	Brachypodium pinnatum	✓	–	✓	–	–	–	–	–	–	–	–	–	–	–	✓	–
	Briza media	✓	–	–	–	–	–	–	–	–	–	✓	✓	✓	✓	–	–
	Bromopsis erecta	✓	–	–	✓	–	–	–	–	–	–	–	–	–	–	–	–
	Bromus commutatus	–	–	✓	✓	✓	✓	–	✓	✓	–	–	–	–	–	–	–
	Cynosurus cristatus	✓	✓	✓	✓	✓	✓	✓	✓	✓	✓	–	✓	✓	✓	✓	✓
	Dactylis glomerata	✓	✓	✓	✓	✓	✓	✓	✓	✓	✓	✓	✓	✓	✓	✓	✓
	Deschampsia cespitosa	✓	✓	–	–	–	–	–	✓	–	✓	–	–	–	–	✓	✓
	Elytrigia repens	–	–	–	–	–	–	–	–	✓	✓	–	–	–	✓	✓	–
	Festuca pratensis	–	–	✓	✓	–	✓	✓	✓	✓	✓	✓	✓	–	✓	✓	✓
	Holcus lanatus	✓	✓	✓	✓	✓	✓	✓	✓	✓	✓	✓	✓	✓	✓	✓	✓
	Hordeum secalinum	–	–	–	–	–	✓	✓	–	–	–	–	–	–	–	–	–
	Koeleria macrantha	–	–	–	–	–	–	–	–	–	–	–	–	–	–	–	–
	Lolium perenne	–	✓	✓	✓	✓	✓	✓	✓	✓	✓	✓	✓	✓	✓	✓	✓
	Phleum bertolonii	–	–	–	✓	✓	✓	–	–	–	–	–	–	–	–	–	✓
	Phleum pratense	–	–	–	–	–	–	–	–	–	✓	✓	–	–	–	–	–
	Poa annua	–	✓	–	–	–	–	✓	✓	–	–	–	–	✓	✓	–	✓
	Poa pratensis	✓	✓	✓	✓	✓	✓	✓	✓	✓	✓	✓	✓	✓	✓	✓	✓
	Poa trivialis	–	–	–	–	–	✓	✓	✓	✓	–	✓	✓	✓	✓	✓	✓
	Trisetum flavescens	✓	–	–	✓	–	✓	✓	–	✓	✓	✓	✓	✓	✓	✓	✓
Polygalaceae	Polygala vulgaris	✓	–	–	–	–	–	–	–	–	–	–	✓	✓	✓	–	–
Polygonaceae	Rumex acetosa	–	✓	✓	✓	✓	✓	✓	✓	✓	✓	✓	✓	✓	✓	✓	✓
	Rumex acetosella	–	–	–	–	–	–	–	–	–	–	–	✓	✓	✓	–	–
Primulaceae	Primula veris	✓	–	✓	–	–	✓	✓	–	✓	–	–	✓	✓	✓	–	–
Ranunculaceae	Anemone nemorosa	–	✓	–	–	–	–	–	–	–	–	–	–	–	–	–	–
	Ranunculus acris	✓	✓	✓	✓	✓	✓	✓	✓	✓	✓	✓	✓	✓	✓	✓	✓
	Ranunculus bulbosus	–	✓	✓	✓	✓	✓	✓	✓	✓	✓	–	✓	✓	✓	✓	✓
	Ranunculus ficaria	–	✓	✓	✓	✓	✓	✓	✓	–	–	–	✓	✓	✓	✓	✓
	Ranunculus repens	✓	✓	✓	✓	✓	✓	✓	✓	✓	✓	✓	✓	✓	✓	✓	✓
Rosaceae	Agrimonia eupatoria	✓	–	–	–	–	–	✓	–	✓	–	–	–	–	–	–	–
	Alchemilla vulgaris	–	–	–	–	✓	–	–	–	–	–	✓	✓	✓	–	✓	–
	Aphanes arvensis	–	–	–	–	–	–	–	–	✓	–	–	✓	–	–	–	–
	Filipendula ulmaria	✓	–	✓	✓	–	–	✓	✓	✓	✓	–	–	–	–	✓	✓
	Filipendula vulgaris	✓	–	–	–	–	–	✓	✓	✓	–	–	–	–	–	–	–
	Potentilla anserina	–	–	✓	✓	✓	✓	–	✓	✓	–	–	–	✓	✓	✓	✓
	Potentilla erecta	–	–	–	–	✓	–	–	–	–	–	–	✓	–	–	✓	✓
	Potentilla reptans	✓	–	–	✓	✓	✓	✓	✓	✓	–	✓	✓	✓	✓	✓	✓
	Sanguisorba minor ssp. minor	✓	–	✓	✓	✓	✓	✓	✓	✓	–	✓	✓	✓	✓	✓	✓
Rubiaceae	Cruciata laevipes	✓	–	–	–	–	✓	✓	–	✓	–	–	✓	✓	✓	✓	✓
	Galium mollugo	–	–	–	–	–	–	–	✓	✓	–	–	–	–	–	–	–
	Galium verum	✓	–	✓	✓	✓	✓	✓	✓	✓	–	✓	✓	✓	✓	✓	✓
	Sherardia arvensis	–	–	–	–	–	–	–	–	✓	–	–	✓	✓	–	–	–
Saxifragaceae	Saxifraga granulata	–	✓	✓	✓	✓	✓	–	–	–	–	–	–	✓	–	–	–
Scrophulariaceae	Euphrasia nemorosa	✓	–	–	–	–	–	–	–	–	–	–	–	✓	–	–	–
	Linaria vulgaris	–	–	–	–	–	–	–	–	–	✓	✓	–	–	–	–	–
	Odontites vernus	–	–	–	–	✓	–	✓	✓	✓	✓	–	–	–	–	–	–
	Pedicularis sylvatica	–	–	–	–	–	–	–	–	–	–	–	✓	–	✓	✓	✓
	Rhinanthus minor	✓	–	–	–	–	–	✓	✓	–	–	–	–	–	–	–	–
	Veronica arvensis	–	–	–	–	–	–	–	–	–	–	–	✓	✓	–	–	–
	Veronica chamaedrys	✓	✓	✓	✓	✓	✓	✓	✓	✓	✓	✓	✓	✓	✓	✓	✓
	Veronica officinalis	–	–	–	–	–	–	–	–	–	–	–	–	–	–	–	✓
	Veronica serpyllifolia	–	✓	–	–	–	–	✓	✓	✓	–	✓	✓	✓	–	–	–
Violaceae	Viola hirta	✓	–	–	–	–	–	–	–	–	–	–	–	✓	–	–	–
	Viola riviniana	✓	–	–	–	–	–	–	–	–	–	–	–	✓	–	–	–

River Swere Meadow Sites

A Swere Bank SSSI
B Meadow South of Swerford Park
C Bank above Little Bridge Marsh
D Quarry Spring Meadow
E Ribbon Marsh Meadow
F Wigginton Meanders Meadow
G Peat Marsh Meadow
H Long Marsh Meadow
I Meadows across from The Dingle
J Meadows between The Dingle and Barford
K Meadow between Little Barford Mill and Deddington Mill
L Bank below Manor Farm, Hook Norton
M Bank on north side of Cradle Farm Marsh, Hook Norton
N Bank on south side of Dogwood Marsh, Hook Norton
O Bank below Grounds Farm, Hook Norton
P Meadow at Berryfield Farm, Great Rollright

REFERENCES

1 David J. Bellamy, 1982. *Woodland Walks (Discovering the Countryside with David Bellamy)*. Hamlyn Publishing Group, London, p. 16.

2 Gilbert White, 1981 (first published in 1789). *The Natural History of Selborne*. Thames & Hudson, London, Letter XLI, 1778.

3 *The Encyclopedia Britannica*, 2003. Vol. XIII. Encyclopedia Britannica Corporation, Chicago, p. 997.

4 Arthur Strahler, 1998. *Physical Geography*, 2nd ed. John Wiley & Sons Ltd., New York.

5 E. C. Pielou, 1998. *Fresh Water*. The University of Chicago Press.

6 C. H. Crickman, 1974. *The World of the River*. Macmillan, London.

7 Alan Grant Ogilvie, 1930. *Great Britain: Essays in Regional Geography*. University Press, London, p. 141.

8 Sheet 218 of the Geological Survey of Great Britain (the Rollright Fault and the Swerford Fault).

9 Alan Crossley (ed.) (1983). *A History of the County of Oxford, Vol. IX*, p. 159. *The Victoria History of the Counties of England*, C. R. Elrington (ed.). The University of London Institute of Historical Research, Oxford University Press.

10 C. Henry Warren, 1939. *The English Countryside*. B. T. Batsford, London.

11 F. M. Stenton, 1971. *Anglo-Saxon England*, 3rd ed. Oxford University Press.

12 F. D. Price, 1998. *The Church of St Giles, Wigginton*. Parchment, Oxford.

13 Rudyard Kipling, 1986. *Puck of Pook's Hill*. Piccolo Books, p. 17.

14 John Blair, 1998. *Anglo-Saxon Oxfordshire*. Sutton Publishing Ltd., Stroud, Gloucestershire.

15 P. M. Thorpe, R. L. Otlet and M. M. Sweeting, 1980. *Hydrological Implications from 14C Profiling of UK Tufa*. In: *Radiocarbon*, Vol. 22, No. 3, pp. 897-908.

16 A. R. Clapham, T. G. Tutin and D. M. Moore, 1987. *Flora of the British Isles*, 3rd ed. Cambridge University Press.

17 *The New Shorter Oxford English Dictionary*, 1993. Vol. 2, 3rd ed. Oxford University Press, New York.

18 Tom Chester, 2002, personal communication.

19 Robin Buxton, 2002, personal communication.

20 *The Encyclopedia Britannica*, 2003. Vol. XV. Encyclopedia Britannica Corporation, Chicago, p. 884.

21 Camilla Lambrick, 2002, personal communication.

22 John Killick, Roy Perry and Stan Woodell, 1998. *The Flora of Oxfordshire*. Pisces Publications, Newbury, Berkshire.

23 Stuart W. Frost, 1959. *Insect Life and Insect Natural History*, 2nd revised ed. Dover Publications Inc., New York. Illustrations in the Crayfish and Other Invertebrates chapter redrawn from Frost.

24 *Book of the British Countryside*, 1973. Drive Publications Ltd., London, for the Automobile Association.

25 Henry David Thoreau, 1991 (first published in 1836). *Walking*. Beacon Press, Boston, Massachusetts, p. 98.

26 Killick et al., op. cit., p. 37.

27 Clapham et al., op. cit.

28 Crossley (ed.), op. cit.: *Wigginton*.

29 Oliver Rackham, 1989. *The History of the Countryside*. J. M. Dent & Sons, London.

30 Blair, op. cit., p. 130.

31 M. O. Hill, J. O. Mountford, D. B. Roy and R. G. H. Bunce, 1999. *Ellenberg's indicator values for British plants*. ECOFACT Vol. 2, Technical Annex. Centre for Ecology and Hydrology, Natural Environment Research Council.

32 J. S. Rodwell (ed.), 1995. *British Plant Communities*, Vol. 5: *Maritime Communities and Vegetation of Open Habitats*. Cambridge University Press, p. 434.

33 A. G. Tansley, 1946. *Introduction to Plant Ecology*, 2nd ed. Allen & Unwin, London.

34 *The New Shorter Oxford English Dictionary*, 1993. Vol. I, 3rd ed. Oxford University Press, New York.

35 Julian Barbour, 2002, personal communication.

36 Charles Singer, E. J. Holmyard, A. R. Hall and Trevor I. Williams (eds.), 1956. *A History of Technology*, Vol. II: *The Mediterranean Civilizations and the Middle Ages, c. 700 B.C. to c. A.D. 1500*. Oxford University Press, New York, p. 610.

37 Ibid., p. 596.

38 Ibid.

39 Crossley (ed.), op. cit., p. 165.

40 Margaret M. Wheat, 1967. *Survival Arts of the Primitive Paiutes*. University of Nevada Press.

41 Killick et al., op. cit.

42 J. S. Rodwell (ed.) 1995. *British Plant Communities*, Vol. 4: *Aquatic Communities, Swamps and Tall-Herb Fens*. Cambridge University Press, p. 153.

43 Michael Proctor, Peter Yeo and Andrew Lack, 1996. *The Natural History of Pollination*. Timber Press, Portland, Oregon, p. 85.

44 Rackham, op. cit.

45 Christopher O'Toole, 1995. *Alien Empire*, Harper Collins, London, p. 110.

46 Ibid., pp. 56-7.

47 Crossley (ed.), op. cit., p. 107.